Lost and Found at Christmas

Caroline Grimshaw
Illustrated by Pam Smy

ELEMENT
CHILDREN'S BOOKS

SHAFTESBURY, DORSET · BOSTON, MASSACHUSETTS · MELBOURNE, VICTORIA

To Joyce, Charles and Ian
– Thanks for Christmas memories –
and Steve – for the Christmas memories we'll make.

© Element Children's Books 1999
Text © Caroline Grimshaw 1999
Illustrations © Pam Smy 1999

First published in Great Britain in 1999 by
Element Children's Books
Shaftesbury, Dorset SP7 8BP

Published in the USA in 1999 by
Element Books, Inc.
160 North Washington Street,
Boston MA 02114

Published in Australia in 1999 by
Element Books and distributed by
Penguin Australia Limited,
487 Maroondah Highway, Ringwood,
Victoria 3134

Cover design by Mandy Sherliker.
Typeset by DTG Design, Dorchester.
Printed and bound in Great Britain by Creative Print and Design.

British Library Cataloguing in Publication data available.
Library of Congress Cataloging in Publication data available.

ISBN 1 902618 67 X

Contents

CHAPTER ONE

Peace on Earth

They had gone off to fight for their country, without really knowing what that meant. Thousands of men, dressed, drilled, and determined to be home by Christmas. It was a long time ago – it was 1914 and there they all were on Christmas Eve – frozen and a little frightened. No candles, no cakes, no festive feast with all the trimmings, no family at all. The British and German troops had built their trenches – deep muddy ditches, full of fear – and that is where they sat, waiting, wondering. Between the trenches lay a space that neither side had seized: "no man's land."

The stars were like diamonds in the deep, dark sky. They twinkled like tiny lights on a family Christmas tree.

John raised his weary head to gaze up at them. His mind flickered back to better days: dancing friends, smiling family faces, hands outstretched to give and receive gifts. The look of wonder on a young child's face as an opened box reveals a rocking horse with a mane and tail made from real horse's hair! He rocked backward and forward in time with his daydream as the young child swayed on his prize present. His face moved to smile, but his skin was too cold, too set to make smiling easy. His eyes were hard and bright, staring into the future as the dream from the past came to an abrupt end.

In the face of danger and loneliness people often become sentimental – they look back to better, brighter times. He was human, after all. They all were. How hard to spend Christmas away from the ones he loved. Surely the enemy, the German soldiers on the other side of "no man's land," shared his emotions this Christmas Eve.

The silence was suddenly broken. A voice drifted into the space between the two groups of soldiers. It hung in the air and then fell, only to be picked up by another voice. Others joined in, spirits without bodies, just floating in the darkness. The British and German troops were calling out greetings to each other across the gap between the trenches. John was stunned – it was just like being at home on Christmas Day: sharing season's greetings with friends and neighbors. He opened his mouth to join in, but his throat was dry, he was empty of words.

The soldier closed his eyes and was transported back to a Christmas Eve nearly twenty years earlier. A small child's face, his own, basking in the soft sounds of *Silent Night*, sung by his mother to help him sleep. He could

hear her breathing between the lines of the carol, he could smell baking in the kitchen ready for the next day's feast. He felt safe and thrilled at the same time.

Lost in the past, he began to hum along with his mother, then the words came into his mind and out of his mouth. *Silent Night, Holy Night* drifted through the darkness. He could hear other voices around him, joining in with his. Then the tune was taken up across the gap between the trenches and to the other side. Now different words, but the same tune, the same feeling, mingled in the cool, still air.

The voices rose higher and higher as if calling to the stars. And leading them all were the kind, familiar tones of his mother's voice. The soldier felt her gazing down at him – for a moment he was home.

Then movement, bodies stirring, soldiers leaving the protective walls of their trenches, men from both sides gingerly scrambling into the divide. "No man's land" had become everyman's land as German and British troops shook hands and shared stories and gifts. Some soldiers even set up a game of soccer, right there in front of the trenches!

The trenches had been touched by a magic that was in itself a Christmas gift to all the people present. Wherever you are, whatever is going on around you, never forget that Christmas is a time for giving and sharing.

What Does Christmas Mean to You?

Christmas is a time of miracles, from the first miraculous event (the birth of a very important baby in a stable) to that warm and wonderful glow that washes over us when we see the fairy on top of the Christmas tree, or hear the soft sounds of *Silent Night* sung under lamplight on a frosty winter night. People all over the world find the time to stop for a moment, take stock, and share in this worldwide celebration . . . some because they wish to celebrate the birth of Jesus Christ; others just want to find time to sit and stare, look back, peer forward. They may want to think about nature and the seasons. The magic of Christmas that has skipped through the centuries has survived because people want to keep it alive.

- **CHRISTMAS:** the smell of pine needles, the sparkle of tinsel in the twilight. Stealing a glance through others' half-closed curtains and peeking at warm light flickering on contented faces.

- **CHRISTMAS:** family and friends arriving from all corners of the world, bearing glittering gifts, laughing, chatting, sharing memories and news.

- **CHRISTMAS:** weaving your way through eerily empty streets, a location lodged somewhere in the back of your mind: a place where for one night you will be welcome and warm.

- **CHRISTMAS:** a puppy, with a wagging tail, looking lost and forlorn, abandoned and alone on the night before Christmas.

- **CHRISTMAS:** kings on camels, glimpsing the past: a star as their backdrop, as they travel across deserts on their journey from the East.

 12

They had been traveling for twelve days, following that bright light in the sky, believing it to be a sign that someone special was about to be born. There were three of them, they were wise men, sometimes called Magi, and they had set out from the East. Before they left they had carefully packed precious gifts for a child they knew had just been born; they were gifts of glittering gold, frankincense – a kind of incense – and myrrh, used to make perfumes. Would that lone star lead them to the little baby with the big future? The star in the dark sky was so intensely bright that they could not have lost their way. But, they murmured, they must be lost – surely the child could not be in a cruelly cold animal's stable? Peering into the place, they saw a scene that

13

reassured them: the light around the child was brighter than the shining star. They had found the king they were looking for.

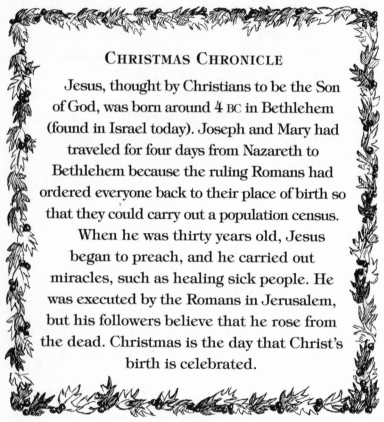

CHRISTMAS CHRONICLE

Jesus, thought by Christians to be the Son of God, was born around 4 BC in Bethlehem (found in Israel today). Joseph and Mary had traveled for four days from Nazareth to Bethlehem because the ruling Romans had ordered everyone back to their place of birth so that they could carry out a population census.

When he was thirty years old, Jesus began to preach, and he carried out miracles, such as healing sick people. He was executed by the Romans in Jerusalem, but his followers believe that he rose from the dead. Christmas is the day that Christ's birth is celebrated.

Who Invented Christmas?

People have celebrated at this time of the year for thousands of years.

Before Christmas even existed – before Christ had been born – people felt the need to celebrate and be most joyous when the earth seemed at its lowest ebb. The dark nights, the bare branches of the trees, and the barren earth encouraged them to find new hope in a new year. This midwinter holiday was taken over by Christian followers.

The word "Christmas" is made up of two words: Christ's Mass. This is the name of the Christian church service that celebrates the birth of Christ. By the year 1100 Christmas was the most important festival for Christians, but they borrowed many ancient traditions for their own celebrations. Before Christianity, many people followed pagan religions, worshiping objects, including the oak tree, as symbols of their gods. The story goes that Martin Luther – an important, learned German scholar, who changed the way people behaved in churches – was the first to cut down a fir tree and bring it indoors to decorate at Christmas.

In ancient Rome, Saturnalia was a time for fun and frivolities, when people let down their guard. The rich gave gifts to the poor, and there was dancing, and games and feasts.

In Britain, it was not until 1880 that Christmas Day was a holiday in England and Wales (and not until 1900 in Scotland). Before that date children had to go to school on Christmas Day.

In Britain it was the Victorians who really invented the traditional Christmas that we still enjoy today.

Do you have the Christmas Spirit?

1) It is October, and the first plastic trees are being dusted off and placed in your favorite store windows. What do you think?

■ How nice! My favorite time of year is just around the corner.

● Tired old trees – no wonder we've all given up on Christmas.

✳ What happened to that purple jacket I was looking at last week?

2) The hottest pop star is scheduled to turn on the Christmas lights in your town. Do you:

✳ Deliberately stay in and watch TV, leaving your friends to go there alone?

● Think to yourself, "If I happen to go by I'll take a look at the action"?

■ Call all your friends and get a group together to go down and check it out?

3) Carol singers knock at your door. You know for a fact that one of them is someone you've had a crush on forever. What do you do?

✳ Dash to the door, smile sweetly,

and hand over a large amount of cash.

■ Get so excited you join in, forgetting that you really can't carry a tune.

● Open the door and offer them a large amount of money if they sing the latest chart hit.

4) Your mother has told you that your brother wants a new skateboard. If you buy him one, you'll never be able to afford that new outfit you had your heart set on. Do you:

■ Think, "There's only one Christmas this year, and my brother deserves to have what he wants – I'll buy the skateboard for him"?

● Ask your mother to chip in a little cash and promise to pay her back by helping her cook on Christmas Day?

✳ Think, "I'll tell her they're sold out of the one he likes and buy him something cheaper"?

5) The big day has dawned. It is only 8 a.m. and everyone wants to get up and open presents. What do you do?

✳ Refuse to move and tell them to start without you.

■ Leap out of bed and start the present opening yourself.

● Ask them to bring you breakfast in bed and tell them you'll join them in half an hour.

6) Everyone's opening presents, and it's your turn. You open one from Great-Aunt Agnes, which turns out to be the most hideous sweater you've ever seen. Do you:

■ Laugh, put it on, and demand that someone take a photo as a memento of the sweater's awfulness?

● Put it aside quietly, figuring you can donate it to charity after Christmas?

✳ Scrunch it up and fling it into a corner, muttering angrily about how ugly it is?

7) Everyone wants to play a board game, but you know you're no good at them. What do you do?

● Suggest you play in teams and pair up with someone smart.

■ Set up the board and get right into the game.

✳ Mumble something about being tired, ignore the game, and flick through a magazine.

What Do You Really Feel?

Each answer has a symbol next to it. When you look at the answers you have chosen, the symbol that appears the most often will tell you how you seem to feel about Christmas!

■ Warm and fuzzy

This is your favorite time of year. You're brimming with Christmas spirit. Whatever is happening, you make sure you enjoy this special time of year.

● A little lukewarm

You'll do your part – after all, you don't want to hurt anyone's feelings – but you're not going to go out of your way and get soppy about Christmas, unless there's something in it for you!

✱ Chillingly cool

You can't stand Christmas and go out of your way to make sure everyone knows it. Who cares if you spoil it for everyone else? They should all give it up, just like you have! Bah Humbug!

19

Trudi the Truant Turkey

The spotlights filled the gloom of the cool and crisp winter night. They shone out as a warning to foxes, blazing the message: STAY AWAY FROM HERE. But the generator that powered the lights was running low on fuel, and farmer Ollie Baker had set out to refill it – with all his other problems, the last thing he wanted was a gang of hungry foxes grabbing his turkeys.

And what a gigantic problem he had. Should he cancel Christmas this year? Should he bid farewell to the money he could earn from selling his turkeys for all those festive feasts? Or should he spare them all, in order to save Trudi, his favorite pet and best bird?

Why, oh why, had Trudi put herself in such danger? And at a time like this too! Just a week before Christmas – what a time to escape from her pen and hide among 1,200 identical birds, destined for the dinner table in just a few hours. The farmer was distraught.

For eleven weeks he had grown more and more fond of Trudi. She had arrived as a tiny turkey, feeble and so terribly small. Ollie knew right away that if he put her with the other birds she would be bullied and pecked. She might have been bound for the slaughterhouse before the year was through, but just then he could not bear to see her suffer in any way at all!

So, in his spare time, Ollie began to construct her a private palace – her own special quarters. He fed her and took her for walks to give her exercise, and he started to think of her more as a pet than as a way to make money. Sometimes at night they would stroll around the farm, gazing at the fleeting clouds, shivering together in the night air and staring up at the glowing spotlights, knowing that while they were shining brightly, the farm was safe and sound.

But now, where was she? LOST – just one in over 1,000! Ollie had tried in vain to lure her back with sweet-corn – her favorite snack – and for four hours a day, when his farm work was done, he had searched through the sea of feathers and faces for Trudi.

That was a week ago, and the time was coming for him to make his decision. He had to sell the turkeys – the orders were in, and his farm needed the money. What should he do? Ollie shuddered. His imagination drew a cruel, clear picture of Trudi – stuffed, sizzling, surrounded by roast vegetables and all the trimmings. He saw the flash of the silver carving knife, the cold steel reflecting the faces of a family, all licking their lips, relishing the moment, hungry for their feast. Trudi was lost – and so was he.

Sure, he was young, only eighteen years old. Some would say he was too sentimental to run a farm, but would you put *your* pampered pet on the Christmas menu? He looked up at the lights in the darkness and his eyes misted over. It was perfectly peaceful: all his birds were asleep in their huts.

Then, he saw it – a shuffling silhouette. Ollie narrowed his eyes and peered. Was it a fox sneaking around the grounds, looking for food of its own? The

shape moved again. There was something familiar about the movement in the darkness – what was it? Quietly, determined not to frighten whatever was out there, Ollie took one step forward. Then, the miracle happened: a turkey calmly waddled toward him, and it was that waddle that made his heart leap. Only one turkey he had ever known moved like that: it had to be Trudi, joining him on his night-time stroll.

Ollie dashed toward her, and she didn't run away. Carefully, he lifted her into the circle of light thrown onto the ground by the spotlight. He raised her wings. There they were, the white patterns that he had seen so many times before. The farmer gently stroked Trudi's feathers, and she looked pretty pleased to see him, too; it must have been tough out there with all the big birds, fattened up and ready for Christmas.

The next day Trudi was back in her pen, snacking on sweetcorn and enjoying all the attention. And Ollie was preparing to sell his turkeys. *Now*, he thought, *I'll be able to cook my Christmas dinner without having to worry about eating my favorite bird, and all my customers will get their turkeys as promised.*

● THIS HEARTWARMING TRUE STORY HAPPENED IN 1998 ON A FARM IN CHICHESTER, WEST SUSSEX, UK. HAPPY ENDINGS FOR ALL, UNLESS OF COURSE YOU WERE ONE OF THE 1,200 TURKEYS THAT WERE NOT SO LUCKY!

CHAPTER TWO

Christmas Traditions

The Real Santa Claus

Very many years ago, our ancestors held midwinter festivals, which featured a goblinlike character dressed in green. He represented spring and the new beginning that was just months away. It is this character who was probably transformed into Saint Nicholas and then Santa Claus in the USA and UK.

Saint Nicholas, a bishop from Myra, in the place we call Turkey today, was born in 280 in Patara and died on December 6, 345. He was famous for helping poor children and eventually became the patron saint of children. The story of this saint was used by the Dutch to create a character called Sinter Klaas, who rode a white horse and swept into homes down chimneys, placing presents in the shoes of good children. When the Dutch traveled to America in the early 17th century, they took Sinter Klaas with them.

In 1891 a poem called *The Night Before Christmas*, written by the American poet Clement Clarke Moore, described Santa as a fat, jolly, white-bearded man who arrived in a sleigh drawn by reindeer and carried a sack bulging with gifts! Our very own vision of Santa Claus had arrived!

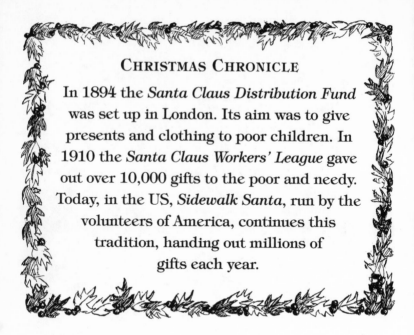

CHRISTMAS CHRONICLE

In 1894 the *Santa Claus Distribution Fund* was set up in London. Its aim was to give presents and clothing to poor children. In 1910 the *Santa Claus Workers' League* gave out over 10,000 gifts to the poor and needy. Today, in the US, *Sidewalk Santa*, run by the volunteers of America, continues this tradition, handing out millions of gifts each year.

Christmas Trees

It was Queen Victoria's husband, Prince Albert, who introduced Christmas trees into Britain. In 1840 he put up the first Christmas tree in Windsor Castle. It was decorated with candles and candy.

The traditional Christmas tree is a fir because the fir tree is triangular and has three sides. This fitted in nicely with the Christian idea of the three sides of God: God the Father, God the Son, and God the Holy Spirit. It also fitted in with the ancient custom of worshiping the tree spirits.

People who care about the planet might say that plucking fir trees from the earth and plunging their roots into a bucket, a log, or a tiny tub, demonstrates the absolute opposite of Christmas goodwill and kindness. The shiny, spiky branches that bring delight for little more than a week are tossed bare, bald, and broken into the street when the festive fever is over. Right now, fashionable folks choose trees made of feathers that flutter when touched. Others use live trees and carefully replant them after Christmas. If you had to decide between the arty artificial and the real thing, what would you choose?

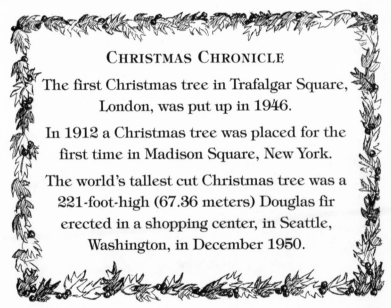

CHRISTMAS CHRONICLE

The first Christmas tree in Trafalgar Square, London, was put up in 1946.

In 1912 a Christmas tree was placed for the first time in Madison Square, New York.

The world's tallest cut Christmas tree was a 221-foot-high (67.36 meters) Douglas fir erected in a shopping center, in Seattle, Washington, in December 1950.

Stockings

Why hang up a stocking? The answer is in this tale of lost fortune and found hope and happiness. When Saint Nicholas inherited a great deal of money, he decided he wanted to use it to help people in need. He discovered that three daughters of a man who had lost everything, were in terrible need of money for their dowries – the money that they had to give their husbands-to-be. Without this money they would never be able to get married. So Saint Nicholas visited their home and threw bags of gold into their stockings, which were hanging up to dry near an open window. Today, we hang up our stockings hoping that someone will fill them with whatever we need to make our dreams come true, or, at the very least, a few bits and pieces that will keep us happy for a little while!

Candles

Light a little candle at Christmas and switch on the light in your world. Why do we do this? Because centuries ago in the gloom of winter, people lit fires and candles to celebrate the birth of the sun and the beginning of a brand-new year. Christians then borrowed the idea, pronouncing that Jesus was the "Light of the World." For some people a lit candle is a symbol of the bright shining star over Bethlehem – the star that lit up the sky when Jesus was born.

Today we arrange little lights on our Christmas trees, which are powered by electricity. These were first used in 1882. They were invented in the USA by Edison's Electric Light Company.

Gifts

People have been giving gifts for 10,000 years. In the New Stone Age our ancestors had taken up agriculture, saving supplies of food to see them through the winter months. At midwinter they arranged a celebration, because they knew the worst was over and spring was on its way. Farmers shared what they had with each other, and these were the first midwinter gifts.

Giving was thought to be a way of showing you cared for and supported the person who received your gifts. Sharing gifts can make the links between people stronger. Selecting something special for someone shows you understand who they are and what they like. People feel that they belong when they receive, and that makes them feel warm all over!

Here is a list of easy things that you can do to help create a warm and happy glow in your own heart this Christmas:

- Contact a charity, and offer them a donation.

- Visit someone old in your neighborhood. Take them a little present. It doesn't matter how small your gift is – just the act of opening it will cheer up your neighbor!

- Take time to share Christmas with your family. Talk to them about what you have done this year and what you want to do next. Offer to help out with the Christmas chores!

- If you don't have much cash to buy presents, you could make something instead. Write a simple poem or draw a picture that sums up why the person receiving the present is so special to you.

- Make contact with older people and ask them to share their memories with you. Find out how much Christmas has changed for them. You could take a trip to a local museum – many have shops set up as they would have been 100 years ago. They will give you a good idea of what people bought as gifts at that time. You may be able to visit an archive: a place where memorabilia, records, and documents from the past are kept. Secondhand shops may stock old books and magazines. Take a look at the advertisements – knowing a little bit about the past will help you understand the future.

Whether you like to follow traditions or invent new ways of doing things, Christmas should be a time when you

can relax, look back, and make a link with the past, in order to take a little something to the future.

Crackers

In Britain, Australia, and some other parts of the English-speaking world, pop-open party favors known as crackers are an essential part of Christmas celebrations. The excitement, the anticipation . . . what's going to be inside your cracker? The moment just before you pull it is the best. Then *crackle*, out pops the tissue-paper hat, a tiny toy, and a not-very-good joke. Crackers make a Christmas meal! Well, that's what Tom Smith thought, when he invented them in 1846. He just wrapped some of his candy up with paper hats, toys, and the thing that makes the crackers crack, and sold them!

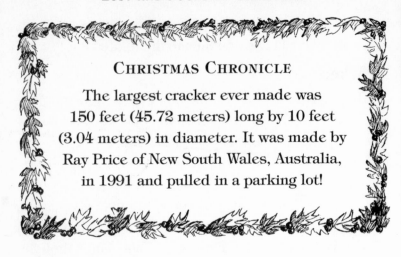

CHRISTMAS CHRONICLE

The largest cracker ever made was 150 feet (45.72 meters) long by 10 feet (3.04 meters) in diameter. It was made by Ray Price of New South Wales, Australia, in 1991 and pulled in a parking lot!

Celebrations

Who celebrates and who does not?

Christmas Eve – and across the world people come together at candle-lit midnight services to celebrate the magic of Christ's birth. Meanwhile, people who have no real interest in a religious message can find their feeling of warmth by gazing into the fire, placing a last perfectly wrapped present under the twinkling tree, or sharing a few jokes with their friends. But what happens if you believe in something completely different?

"I go along with the celebrations at Christmas – in this country it's hard to get out of it! But Buddhists don't believe in the Christmas message, because it's a Christian festival. Although we may think that Jesus was a good man, he is not our God. Our religion is based on the teachings of a prince called Siddhartha Gautama. When he was twenty-nine he gave up all his wealth and started to meditate and preach. He took on a new name – Buddha – which means "the enlightened one." We are more into the spirit of the New Year, which we celebrate because it's the time for a fresh start, when you think about all the things that you really want to do that you haven't yet done. It's also the time when you can become determined to change the things that you want to change in your life. I chant every day in the morning and the evening. When we want to change something in a big way, such as at New Year, we will chant more."

TEACHER WORKING IN THE UK – BUDDHIST

"We do not celebrate Christmas at all. It is not part of our religion. I work in the shop and greet people in a friendly way, but I would not wish them a Merry Christmas. Christmas Day is like any other day for us – except the shop is not open – we relax and spend time with the family. We do not exchange presents."

SHOPKEEPER WORKING IN
THE US – HINDU

"Gifts are given to each other at Christmastime and families get together. It is a time for the children really. If the younger members of my family are in schools with children who are celebrating Christmas, they may feel left out if they have no pre-sents and cannot join in. So we have a present-giving time for them. We have our own festivals that move around depending on the lunar calendar. This is when we celebrate in the way that Christians do at Christmas."

ARCHITECT WORKING IN
CANADA – MUSLIM

Singing

Coming together at Christmas is all about sharing time together. That is what people are doing when they come knocking on your door, drowning out the silence with their carol singing.

A traditional story tells us that the first carols were sung by the angels, announcing the birth of the new baby king – Jesus. Many of the carols that are still sung around the world at Christmastime first appeared in England in the 14th and 15th centuries. The most popular carol today is *Silent Night*, which was written over 180 years ago. This song, which has been translated into nearly three hundred languages, was written by Joseph Mohr in 1816, when he was staying in a village in the Alps in Austria. The story goes that he had to act quickly – he was composing the music for a Christmas Eve service, and the church mice were chewing away at the bellows of his organ. It is said that Mohr wrote speedily to finish his task before the organ stopped working!

Today, some of the newer carols are more popular than the older, more traditional ones. Take a look at this top ten:

1 *Silent Night* (33 percent OF VOTES)
2 *Away in a Manger* (12 percent OF VOTES)
3 *Little Donkey* (11 percent OF VOTES)
4 *Good King Wenceslas* (9 percent OF VOTES)
5 *Jingle Bells* (8 percent OF VOTES)
6 *Hark the Herald Angels Sing*
   God Rest Ye Merry Gentlemen } (7 percent OF VOTES)
8 *O Come All Ye Faithful* (6 percent OF VOTES)
9 *In the Bleak Midwinter* (4 percent OF VOTES)
10 *We Three Kings* (3 percent OF VOTES)

THE INFORMATION WAS TAKEN FROM A SURVEY CARRIED OUT BY A BRITISH NATIONAL NEWSPAPER (THE *EXPRESS*) AND PUBLISHED ON DECEMBER 5, 1998.

and imagined the world as it should be. He
cribed what he thought was lost in the world, and
at needed to change to make the world a brighter
ce for everyone. He did this by writing stories.

Some of Dickens's depictions and descriptions of
ristmas have helped paint the image of Christmas
t we have in our minds today. Christmas was tradi-
nally a time to relax and be merry. Dickens described
ristmas at Dingley Dell in one of his books, *Pickwick
pers*, written in 1836, as a "merry old time."

In Dickens's last story, *The Mystery of Edwin Drood*,
blished in 1870, Drood was murdered on Christmas
e – an event that seems even more dreadful because
happened so close to Christmas.

Many of Dickens's tales were serialized in newspapers,
hich meant that hundreds of people had a chance to
low them. If you think of these stories in the same way
u might think of the soaps on television today, you'll
t the picture. People were mesmerized by the events
nd the characters of Dickens's tales. They waited for the
ext installment with bated breath! Dickens became so
pular that he was asked to tour the world giving read-
gs from his stories. These readings really moved some
ople in the audience, as this true story shows:

had been a long and arduous journey across
e ocean to the other side of the world, but he had
ade it. There he was in America. *What will they make
f Dickens here?* he thought, as he stood on the

Sensational Christmas Songs

● The most famous popular Christmas song was written in
1942 and was sung by Bing Crosby. It is called *White
Christmas*. Thirty million copies of this song have been
sold (plus 100,000,000 cover versions made by other
people)! Why does the song make people go dreamy?
Because it's overflowing with a glowing nostalgia – looking
back to a time when everything was wonderful and warm!

CHRISTMAS CHRONICLE

London has had eight "white" or snowy
Christmas Days since 1900: 1906, 1917,
1923, 1927, 1938, 1956, 1970, 1981.

Rudolph the Red-Nosed Reindeer was written
by Johnny Marks in 1949. Poor old Rudolph
was ridiculed because of his glowing red
nose. But it was that very nose that came to
the rescue, lighting up the dark skies on
Santa's Christmas Eve journey.

In 1984 a group of famous pop stars formed
a supergroup called Band Aid and recorded
a song called *Do They Know It's Christmas?*
All the money raised was donated to the
Ethiopian Relief Fund, to help people
starving that Christmas in Ethiopia.

Christmas Cards

The best way to brighten up your long-lost friends' festive season is to send them greeting cards. It's also a simple way to remind friends and family that you are out there! The very first Christmas card was printed in 1843. It sold for a shilling (that's 95 pence / $1.50), which was a lot of money at the time! The card was made by a very famous man called Sir Henry Cole. He made a thousand copies and sold them in his shop. The card showed a picture of a happy family and the words read:

"A Merry Christmas and a Happy New Year to You" – a message that has been well used ever since.

In 1840 in Britain the cost of mailing a card anywhere in the country was just one penny. Thousands of people made use of this Penny Post. In the 1860s printing in color was invented, and it became cheaper to mass-produce cards.

By 1877 so many cards were being sent that a British national newspaper – *The Times* – described them as a "social evil." Today, in Britain, more than a billion cards are sent through the mail every December. Imagine what this figure must be worldwide!

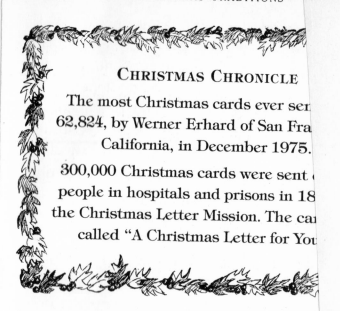

CHRISTMAS CHRONICLE

The most Christmas cards ever sen
62,824, by Werner Erhard of San Fra
California, in December 1975.

300,000 Christmas cards were sent
people in hospitals and prisons in 18
the Christmas Letter Mission. The ca
called "A Christmas Letter for You

Charles Dickens saves Christmas!

Around two hundred years ago, Christma danger of being completely lost and forgotten!

Magazines and newspapers at that time did mention the event. Between 1790 and 1835 newspaper in Britain did not report any Christi ities, and New Year and St. Valentine's Day festi thought to be more important.

Then a few people found Christmas hiding ished it up, and presented it to the world! One people was the writer Charles Dickens, who was 1812 and died in 1870.

Dickens was a man who was determined to the true spirit of Christmas. He looked at the wo

gangplank of the vessel that had been his watery home for so long.

Dickens knew he had put everything into *A Christmas Carol*, which he had finally finished in 1843, and the story had been a huge success. His readers had been deeply affected by the story of Scrooge, the miserable old miser who hated Christmas. They were intrigued that this ghastly fellow had been faced with ghosts from his past, present, and future. Readers had been thrilled with the transformation of a man who at one time could not even bear to celebrate Christmas himself, let alone share it with others. Some had said that the writer was pointing out to the world that the real spirit of Christmas had been lost, and that we are all a little like Scrooge. Well, perhaps he had been gently pushing people in that direction. After all, if we can't open up our lives and think about giving at Christmastime, when can we?

So *A Christmas Carol* had been a success, and Dickens was delighted. He was also pleased that he could share his tale with a new set of people in America.

When Dickens arrived in Boston on Christmas Eve in 1867, he was unsure of the reaction he would receive. The writer intended to read some extracts from *A Christmas Carol* and see how the audience responded.

The room was packed. Faces bright, bubbling, eager to hear his words, greeted Dickens. What better time to read his story than the night before Christmas Day itself?

As Dickens stepped up onto the platform, there was a hush around the room, followed by polite, but warm, handclapping.

The writer looked out at the sea of faces, focusing on one, floating to another, imagining what their own Christmases were like. Then he heard his own voice introduce himself and his Christmas tale. He took a deep breath and began.

The writer's voice carried the lives of his characters across the room and into the hearts and souls of his audience. As they sat, entranced, each person conjured up his or her own image of the scenes described. They all saw in their own minds the poverty of Tiny Tim and his family and the ferocious selfishness of Mr. Scrooge.

The ghosts of Christmas, past, present, and future filled the minds of everyone in the room. What would happen if they themselves were visited by these ghosts? What tales would the ghosts bring?

The emotion of the story showed on the faces of the audience as they listened, rooted to their seats. Faces with frowns, eyes brimming over with tears, hands clasped in suspense – the audience lived every word.

But there was one man in the crowd in Boston that day who sat very still. His face looked unmoved, but Mrs. Fairbanks, holding her husband's hand tightly throughout the evening, knew that

he was deeply affected by what he heard. Hadn't he been saying much the same thing to her? Surely this was the time of year to treat his factory workers, not torment them. They deserved a reward for their hard work through the year. They deserved a holiday.

What tales would his ghosts tell? Was he a man who made people leave their families on Christmas Day to work for him? He thought of his workers, their faces full of strength and concentration, their families waiting at home. His mind was still full of these pictures when he realized that the story was over, and the narrator's stream of words had been replaced by a roar of applause. The audience was on its feet – some were cheering, others were stamping their feet! He had never seen anything like it!

As Dickens stood, moved by the reception, quietly gripping his leather-bound book, he turned toward Mr. Fairbanks, the wealthy and successful factory owner. Their eyes met for a few seconds, and through the din, Mr. Fairbank saw Dickens mouth these words: "Merry Christmas to you all."

The next day, Dickens moved on to a new audience. But he had sown the seeds of Christmas spirit in the hearts of everyone who had been in the room the night before. And Mr. Fairbanks? He was so moved by Dickens's words that the following day – Christmas Day – he closed down his factory, giving his workers a holiday, and he never opened his factory at Christmas again!

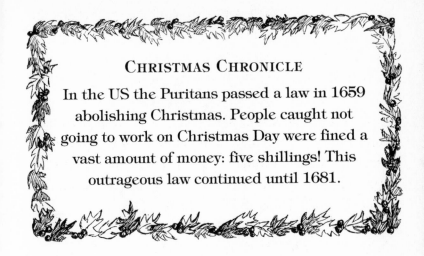

CHRISTMAS CHRONICLE

In the US the Puritans passed a law in 1659 abolishing Christmas. People caught not going to work on Christmas Day were fined a vast amount of money: five shillings! This outrageous law continued until 1681.

In America, another writer was busy reminding people that Christmas should not be forgotten. In *Sketch Book* (1819) Washington Irving describes children hurrying home for the Christmas holidays – the thrill and excitement filling the air.

So, from 1900 onward Christmas has been the most important festival of the year. Today Santa is in the stores from October and the pressure is on for us all to buy more, eat more, have more. But the spirit of giving and goodwill is intact. When you half-close your eyes and think about Christmas, it is probably a picture of the past that you see – a traditional Christmas found for us by two great writers.

CHAPTER THREE

Lost and Alone

It was dusk, a time chosen by some people in the hope that the darkness will hide their evil deeds. The shape stumbled, shifted, and plunged forward, suspending the sack upside down and giving it a cruel shake.

A soft yelp, drowned out by a rough cough that cut the cool air – more tactics for covering up cruelty. Then the shape skulked away, leaving only the stars and moon to protect the lost ones, abandoned to the night.

Christmas is not such a winter wonderland when you're dumped painfully in the prickles of a holly bush. The poor little pup felt the thorns rip into her soft skin, as tiny blood balls, like berries, appeared on her silvery, still-fluffy fur. She shuddered, whined woefully, and clambered cautiously out of the evergreen, looking for a kinder place to rest.

Christmas Eve: it should have been the brightest and best day of her life – her first Christmas. Yet, here she was, left cold and shivering in a stranger's garden.

What went wrong? What had she done?

It had been her first day in her new home. The family had turned up the heating and gathered around the TV. She remembered a little boy, glued to the screen, mesmerized by the make-believe magic of Disney dogs and cats. The tiny tot hissed as the crazy and cruel baddie seized the Dalmatian pups, determined to make herself a dashing new coat using the dogs' fur.

A loud bang, a door slamming shut, and then chaos. The pup felt the hulk lumber toward her. The floorboards creaked, the tinsel-clad tree toppled over, and the terrified child stood open-mouthed, wide-eyed as his father seized and shook his pup, his Christmas treat, his new best friend.

Then screams, and streams of words, slurred speech, muffled and lost, as the pup was plunged into a coarse, smelly sack.

Crash – the sack hit something hard.
Bang – the front gate snapped shut.
Then silence.

Her miserable attacker could hardly walk – several times he stopped suddenly to catch his breath. Finally the pup was released, abandoned. No Christmas cheer, no children dear, patting her and stroking her.

What had she done?

The pup cowered and cringed and curled up under the

lantern that lit up the front porch of the nearby house. Her bones were frozen. The blood berries on her fur had dried up and turned a dull brown.

Suddenly she heard the sound of music – someone was whistling and coming her way. Should she run or stand her ground? The gate creaked open and a figure stepped up the path, weighed down by brightly colored pack-ages. The pup struggled to her feet and she limply lifted her head. Bright eyes met her tired gaze.

A gentle hand reached

out and stroked her injured frame. Before the pup had time to even consider running for cover she was inside the house, stretched out in front of the flickering flames of a glowing fire. A few morsels of turkey and a kindly pat on the back of the head, and the pup settled down to dream.

It must be Christmas after all!

The pup had been saved by a man with a heart of gold, but sadly, too old to keep a tiny puppy. This dog needed a good home, and the man knew just what to do. He was so angry with whoever had been so cruel. When people abandon their pets this way, they lose what being human is all about, he thought. Humans are creatures with brains and minds – they should know the difference between right and wrong. Sadly, so many people do not.

On Christmas Day he called workers from the RSPCA. The man knew that they would take care of Holly – the name he had given the dog after her ordeal with the prickly bush. They would make sure that Holly would never be left to shiver and suffer alone again.

And what about the man cruel enough to commit such a crime? His Christmas was in tatters. The little boy, his Christmas pet yanked away from him, spent Christmas Day sobbing, scowling, hurt and heartbroken.

THIS IS WHAT DEBBIE WALKER, GREAT AYTON ANIMAL CENTRE'S DEPUTY MANAGER, HAS TO SAY ABOUT SOME PETS' MISERABLE CHRISTMAS EXPERIENCES THAT SHE HAS WITNESSED:

"Sadly, we see cases like this every year. People either hand in dogs before Christmas to make way for relatives or a new pet, or they are given a pet they are unable to care for long-term, and that animal is later dumped. I should imagine Holly is just the start of it, and once the novelty wears off we will have more unwanted pets on our hands. Dogs require a great deal of commitment and should never be bought on impulse or for someone else. I hope people will look at the case of Holly and think twice before making the same mistake next year."

The SPCA, in Dublin, Ireland, found its own way of dealing with the thoughtlessness of people at Christmas: they simply closed their doors. In the three weeks before Christmas in 1998, they refused to rehome animals just because people were tired of them or wanted a new, younger model. They also refused to sell animals until Christmas was over. SPOKESPERSON MAURICE BYRNE SAYS:

"The rush to buy pets in the weeks before Christmas is matched by the rush to return them a week or so after the celebrations."

Do You Have a Pet?

Half of the homes in the UK do! Look at this chart showing the percentage of homes with pets:

Dog: 23.4 percent	Budgie: 3.6 percent
Cat: 21.4 percent	Hamster: 3.2 percent
Goldfish: 9.3 percent	Tropical fish: 2.4 percent
Rabbit: 3.9 percent	Guinea pig: 1.6 percent

Most people are proud of their pets – a survey tells us that 21 percent of all American dog owners love to show off their pet's abilities. They tell us that their dogs can sit, roll over, and shake hands when asked. People love to share the festive fun with a precious pet who is part of the family.

A Pet Is for Life

Some presents you can throw out when they become dull and out-of-date. Some cost a lot of money, but after you've bought them, you only have to pay for more batteries. But giving a pet as a present is a different story. To give your pet what it needs takes time and money. Dogs need regular exercise and companionship. Cats are more independent than dogs, but they get lonely if left alone. Guinea pigs and gerbils need to be with creatures just like them. A golden hamster needs to be kept alone, but must be kept occupied and have toys to play with.

Now take a look at this chart:

WHAT A 12-YEAR-OLD DOG HAS COST THE FAMILY SO FAR:		
One can of dog food for 365 days a year:	£3,504	$5,606
Dry dog food:	£1,080	$1,728
Yearly booster vaccination:	£300	$480
Health insurance:	£810	$1,296
Two-weeks vacation – boarding costs:	£1,200	$1,920
One visit to the vet each year:	£240	$384
Bedding and other equipment:	£100	$160
Total after 12 years:	**£7,234**	**$11,574**
WHAT A 13-YEAR-OLD CAT HAS COST THE FAMILY SO FAR:		
One can of cat food a day:	£2,373	$3,796
One box of dry food a week:	£541	$865
Vaccinations and boosters:	£300	$480
Flea and worm treatment:	£520	$832
Health insurance:	£860	$1,376
Litter:	£2,028	$3,245
Two-weeks vacation – boarding costs:	£845	$1,352
One visit to the vet each year:	£260	$416
Carrier and equipment:	£100	$160
Total after 13 years:	**£7,827**	**$12,522**

THESE ROUGH FIGURES HAVE BEEN TAKEN FROM RSPCA INFORMATION.

That is a lot of money! What do some people do if they can't cope with their new present? They dump it. Tales of animals lost or abandoned always make front-page news around Christmastime.

True stories from Christmas 1998

- A seven-week-old terrier puppy was thrown out of a car in a remote area of South Wales.

- Two ten-week-old kittens were left in a front yard in Sunderland.

- An eight-week-old kitten was found outside an apartment building in Gateshead.

- A twelve-week-old puppy was dumped in a front yard in Middlesborough on Christmas Day.

- "Dumping bins" – a little like recycling bins – which people could use to abandon unwanted pets and stray animals that they found wandering around the streets, have finally been banned. In Smyrna, Tennessee, people had been encouraged to place unwanted animals in concrete bunkers with metal chutes at the front. Animals left there were supposed to be picked up twice a day: if they were not claimed or rehomed within two days they would be destroyed. The Humane Society of the United States (HSUS) is a group that had been campaigning against the dumping bins for three years. The group was delighted that the fight had finally been won.

● Three little kittens were dumped in a box on a canal towpath on a cold winter day. They had always had each other for company and so, when they were taken to the Danemere Animal Sanctuary in Worcestershire, UK, they stuck together. Until just before Christmas. Poor Jaffa was left behind when his playmates,

Scrumpie and Pepper, were adopted by a couple who only wanted two cats – not three. Now Jaffa the ginger cat must wait his turn for a rescuer. Who is out there for him?

● A hamster was found dead in its cage in an empty home. The family had obviously gone away for Christmas, without arranging for someone to take care of their pet.

Animal Rescue

RICHARD MOORE ALSO WORKS AT THE GREAT AYTON ANIMAL CENTRE AS AN ANIMAL CARE ASSISTANT. HE HAS BEEN WORKING WITH THE CATS AND DOGS THERE FOR NEARLY SIX YEARS. RICHARD WORKED ON CHRISTMAS DAY, 1998. HE SHARES HIS STORY:

What's the best thing that has happened in the center?

When a badly treated animal arrives, is looked after, then leaves to go to a good home and at a later date comes back, looking healthy and happy. That's a real highpoint.

How many animals are there at the center?

We have over seventy dogs and between thirty and forty cats, plus thirty rabbits and other creatures from the wild.

What happens on Christmas Day?

The center is closed to the public. So we take the chance to clean up the place. We work from 8:30 in the morning until 5:00. It's an ordinary workday without the public. So we have a chance to spend some time with the animals. We sort out some Christmas treats and toys for them, too. The dogs have a turkey dinner. We try to make it as special as we can for the animals.

What's your favorite Christmas tale?

We found two potbellied pigs abandoned in Hexham by a farmer. They arrived on November 13. We advertised in the local papers, but no one came to claim them, and no one seemed to want to take them off our hands. Then we used TV and national papers to try to find a home for the pigs. And just before Christmas we succeeded! They're going to Whitby in Yorkshire to live on a farm. We didn't really have the space to keep these animals for long. If we hadn't found them a home they would have had to have been slaughtered. The problem was that someone in the area had been breeding potbellied pigs as Christmas presents. So there were a lot of young piglets out there – no one wanted a pair of grown-up pigs.

Match the Pets to the Owners

These animals in an Animal Rescue Center all need new owners for different reasons. Organizations like the RSPCA check that the animal is right for the family and the family is right for the animal before they send rescued creatures off to a new life.

Case Study 1:

WHO ARE THEY?	Elderly man and woman.
OCCUPATION:	Retired.
HOME:	Two-storey house with a large walled yard.
GETTING AROUND:	They have a son with a dog who lives nearby and has a car, but they no longer drive themselves. They love taking brisk walks together in the morning and the evening.

Case Study 2:

WHO ARE THEY?	Energetic man in his early twenties and his girlfriend.
OCCUPATION:	Plumber with his own business – he does not work long hours. His girlfriend also works part-time – three hours a day in an office.
HOME:	Ground-floor apartment with a fenced-in yard.
GETTING AROUND:	He likes to drive and enjoys running – he trains for the marathon each year. She likes gardening.

Case Study 3:

WHO ARE THEY?	Married couple with ten-year-old twins.
OCCUPATION:	Mother takes care of the home; father has a well-paid office job.
HOME:	Large house in the suburbs with a big fenced-in yard.
GETTING AROUND:	They all love to walk, but have a station wagon that the husband drives to work.

Case Study 4:

WHO ARE THEY?	Family with two teenage children.
OCCUPATION:	Mother has a part-time job in a beauty salon.
	Father has a high-powered job in the city.
HOMES:	A luxury penthouse apartment with great views of the city, and a country cottage that they use once a month to "get away from it all."
GETTING AROUND:	They have two big cars – they never walk.

The Rescue Animals

Pet one:
- Eight-year-old cat
- Previous owner, who also had a dog, now lives in a senior citizens' home where pets are not allowed.

Pet two:
- Nine-month-old Dalmatian
- Abandoned
- Fairly lively

Pet three:
- Two-year-old cat
- Stray
- Independent
- Affectionate

Pet four:
- Three-year-old Labrador
- Owner has died
- Used to other animals
- Obedient

Answers

Case Study 1 = paired with pet four:

This elderly man and woman have a big enough house and garden for a dog of this size. If they need to take the animal to the vet by car they can call on their son. They enjoy walking – the dog will be a valuable companion on their daily outings. They could also invite their son and his dog to join them, since their new pet is used to other animals. The dog is not too young and has been well trained – it will not wear them out!

Case Study 2 = paired with pet three:

A cat with an independent spirit would fit the lifestyle of this energetic man and his girlfriend. They have a yard for the cat to play in, and the girlfriend likes the outdoors. Although the man enjoys exercise, he prefers to do it alone – a dog would not be able to accompany him on his training sessions. The couple have enough time to devote to a cat.

Case Study 3 = paired with pet two:

The couple with ten-year-old twins have enough money, time, and energy to devote to a young, lively dog. The family enjoys exercise, but they have a car if they need to take the dog to the vet or to the country for a day out. The mother is there all day to take care of the dog.

Case Study 4 = not paired to a pet

This family is not suited to looking after a dog or cat. Why? A dog could not be left alone in an apartment while the family was at work or school. They have loads of money, but this is not enough to make an animal happy. A cat would be miserable gazing out of a window all day, and it would be in danger if it did try to escape. The teenage children are at an age when they may have other things on their minds: schoolwork, music, makeup, boyfriends and girlfriends. The family moves between two homes, which would be confusing for a pet – pets like to have a settled existence. The family has no interest in exercise or fresh air – they would soon get bored walking a dog. The pet might end up being ignored, or at worst, abandoned.

The Place to Look for a Lost Pet or Find a New Friend

The Dogs' Home, Battersea, London. website: http://www.dogshome.org

In 1860 Mary Tealby was so worried about the number of stray dogs roaming the streets of London, that she set up The Temporary Home for Lost and Starving Dogs in North London. In 1871 the Home moved to Battersea and was renamed: The Dogs' Home, Battersea. Since its opening, the home has provided shelter and care for over 2,801,000 animals. It receives around 9,000 dogs a year, out of which around 2,000 are claimed and 4,000 are rehomed. Cats were first accepted in 1883, and today around 130 cats are housed at any one time. The Bell Mead kennels are used when the Battersea kennels are full.

In preparation for the outside world and a possible owner, the animals are vaccinated, and groomed, and given health checks and behavior classes. All animals are microchipped: a tiny chip, the size of a grain of rice, is placed under the animal's skin so it can be identified if it gets lost. The microchip has a unique identification number which is used to find the owner's details on a computer database.

The Dogs' Home costs around £4 million ($6.4 million) a year to run. Where does this money come from? Donations from people who care.

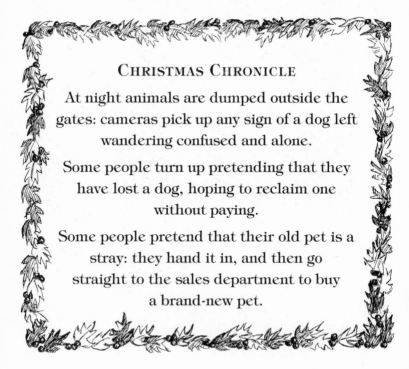

CHRISTMAS CHRONICLE

At night animals are dumped outside the gates: cameras pick up any sign of a dog left wandering confused and alone.

Some people turn up pretending that they have lost a dog, hoping to reclaim one without paying.

Some people pretend that their old pet is a stray: they hand it in, and then go straight to the sales department to buy a brand-new pet.

True Tales from Battersea

- **December 14, 1998:** Santa Claus visited the Dogs' Home, along with eight children and a giant sack. He stayed for two hours, handing out toys and treats to the animals.

- **Christmas Day:** A dog was brought to the home, injured and scared. He had been found wandering around the streets.

63

- **December 30:** A Jack Russell terrier was handed over by a sad man with a letter saying that he had no job and no home. He included a list of what his pet loved and hated.

- **December 31:** Two puppies were brought in because the owners had decided they no longer wanted them.

Meet Martin Martignetti. He has driven a van for The Dogs' Home for sixteen years. Martin works alongside his wife, Pauline – the head driver:

"We get into work at 6 a.m. and check the list of dogs to be collected. This has been faxed through by the police stations. Then we make a list of the dogs to be picked up. Before Christmas we were picking up about twenty-five dogs a day. After Christmas the number is much greater."

Pauline, who has worked for Battersea for twenty-one years, was on duty on Christmas Day:

"I started out at 6 a.m. as usual. Just before Christmas we had picked up a beautiful dog – a bull mastiff – called William, but he had been badly mistreated. He had been the sweetest dog that you could ever wish to meet. He had terrible hips; he could hardly stand. Once he sat down he couldn't stand up again. Someone had cut off his ears. We had to keep him for seven days, because that is policy at the home – just in case someone came to claim him – but we knew that in the end we

would have to put him to sleep. I don't know who would do such a thing, but all we can do is do the best for him while he's with us.

"It was a sad thing to happen at Christmas. But I love my job, and I love dealing with the dogs. I'm addicted to the work: the more I do, the more I want to do. It's not a job that stops at the end of the working day – I've got four dogs running about in my home!"

Pets Lifeline: Caring for Homeless and Lost Dogs

Imagine being lost and alone in a city. The sad, stray dogs that wearily patrol America's city streets need the same loving care as any human being. They need their own lifeline, too. Shelters have been set up to help abandoned pets throughout the USA. This is the story of one of them. *Pets Lifeline* seeks to provide a safe haven for homeless dogs. Staff and volunteers work to make sure that each animal brought to the shelter receives the care, food, medical attention, and exercise that it needs. Then, when the animal is healthy and happy, the group tries to match it with a caring adopter. The group also tries to reunite lost pets with their owners.

Pets Lifeline is run privately, which means that it relies on donations from people and businesses, as well as a band of enthusiastic volunteers who really care about the happiness of the animals at the shelter.

Christmas is the time when the shelter is especially busy. The number of stray and unwanted dogs found and brought to the shelter increases. It is also the time when goodhearted people want to share a bit of the spirit of Christmas with their animal friends. Check out this heartwarming story:

Barney, a two-year-old Labrador, was bought to the shelter. He was found cowering in a dark, damp alley, suffering and in shock. Barney had been battered and bruised and was very frightened. At first the carers at the shelter could not go near him without him whimpering and backing off. But after a few weeks, a volunteer began to notice that if she held out her hand to the dog, he would eventually approach it, sniff it, and then nestle up against it. Barney was a natural cuddler – he just loved to be affectionate. Although he was a little shy at first, Barney was actually a sweet, eager-to-please doggie who just wanted to be fussed over! The dog had obviously also spent time around children in his past, because he warmed to them immediately.

Just days before Christmas, after Barney had been in the shelter for several weeks, a family who had recently lost their own family pet turned up looking for an animal to fill the big hole that is left when a dog that has been part of a loving family dies.

Barney held back when they looked him over, then slowly came forward to cuddle up against the outstretched hand of Janie, the youngest daughter. The family recognized that the dog had a good heart, and that he just needed a little attention to make him feel

at home again. After all the formalities, Barney was taken home in time for the Christmas celebrations.

What Can You Do to Help?

You can join Pets Lifeline or provide a loving home for a stray animal, or simply spread the word about the group. Think about setting up special fundraising events – you could make doggie-themed craft items and sell them to raise money.

When you become a member you will receive a special pet-care card for your wallet, and the Pets Lifeline Newsletter.

Become a volunteer! You could be a Pet Pal. Visit the center and you can select a dog to look after: walk him, groom him, socialize with him. If you haven't got the time, space, or money to be a full-time doggie carer, then you can do it part-time. Become a dog's best friend! (Volunteers under the age of thirteen must complete the Junior Volunteer Application and be accompanied by a parent when at the shelter.)

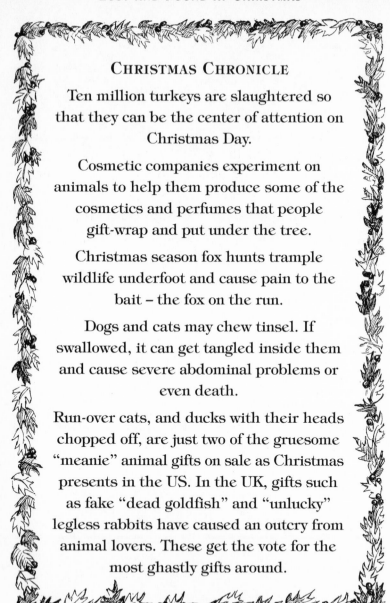

CHRISTMAS CHRONICLE

Ten million turkeys are slaughtered so that they can be the center of attention on Christmas Day.

Cosmetic companies experiment on animals to help them produce some of the cosmetics and perfumes that people gift-wrap and put under the tree.

Christmas season fox hunts trample wildlife underfoot and cause pain to the bait – the fox on the run.

Dogs and cats may chew tinsel. If swallowed, it can get tangled inside them and cause severe abdominal problems or even death.

Run-over cats, and ducks with their heads chopped off, are just two of the gruesome "meanie" animal gifts on sale as Christmas presents in the US. In the UK, gifts such as fake "dead goldfish" and "unlucky" legless rabbits have caused an outcry from animal lovers. These get the vote for the most ghastly gifts around.

Pets Lifeline works really hard to make sure that the right people are matched with the right pets. Adopting a dog or puppy costs just $70 (£44). This money goes toward the cost of spaying or neutering the animal, and making sure it has had its kennel cough and rabies vaccines. It also pays for deworming, a flea bath, and a personalized ID tag for the dog. On top of that, adopters receive a coupon for either two private dog training classes or a seven-session group course.

Contact: Pets Lifeline, P.O. Box 341, Sonoma, CA 95476, Telephone (707) 996-4577, or check out the website on http://www.petslifeline.org

The shelter is located at 19686 Eighth Street East, Sonoma.

Give a Little Bit – It's Better than Taking

Here are two easy things you can do to help animals this Christmas:

- Collect money for Animal Rescue Centers – you could organize a sponsored event.
- Give a friend a special gift this Christmas and help your local zoo. Donate money and adopt an animal.

Hugs for Homeless Animals is an American charity dedicated to caring for homeless animals. Their projects are featured on their website: http://www.h4ha.org/

Snuggles – with the slogan "All I need is a Snuggle and a place to call home" – is one of these projects. It aims to give comfort and security to animals in shelters as they wait for their new homes. Anyone can join.

RAE FRENCH, A SNUGGLES HELPER, SAYS:

"I love animals, even more than I love to crochet (for those who know me, you know that has to be a lot). It breaks my heart when I see animals suffering in any way . . . I had been feeding stray cats that came to my house for food and comfort. These cats were homeless, abandoned by their owners, and my heart ached because I pictured them in their hard, cold cells. So I got the idea of security blankets for the animals and called these blankets "Snuggles." Each animal would get a Snuggle to cuddle up to. At the moment the animals are kept in cold, stainless steel areas with hard plastic flooring. The Snuggles would allow them to have a little rest from the coldness of the place that they are kept in."

Rae has asked people to donate to the project crocheted or knitted blankets – or even the raw materials that can be used to make blankets. It is the perfect Christmas present for a cat in care!

The Hugs for Homeless Animals website also has a Worldwide Shelter Directory, allowing people to find their nearest shelter. Another project, called *Lost and Found Pets*, allows visitors to the site who have lost a pet to download a free Lost Pet poster. Lists of pets that have been found, and those lost across all of America and in other countries, such as Australia, Canada, Italy, and Spain, are stored on the site.

No matter how desperate things may seem, we have to believe that something bright is just around the corner. Take heart from this true story that happened at Christmas 1998 in Hertfordshire, UK:

What is in your trash can? Pieces of paper, boxes and packaging, maybe some potato peelings? Well, just two weeks before Christmas, one woman found an eight-week-old collie shut inside a cardboard box and dumped in her trash can. Just before she put the can out for the garbage collectors, she saw the box move. Carefully she lifted the lid and saw two large, sad, saucerlike eyes gazing at her – the pup had been left there to die. She called the RSPCA, and Inspector Nigel Shelton arrived to help treat the collie. He called her Lilly and took her home and nursed her back to life, getting her ready for a new home and her first Christmas. If that little dog had fallen asleep she would have died of cold – her wriggling saved her life!

CHAPTER FOUR

Missing

Sophie had always found it hard not to be shy. When-ever she walked into a room full of strangers she would become tongue-tied, her cheeks flushed embar-rassingly pink, and she would fix her eyes firmly on the floor. It had been like this for as long as she could remember. Every time she joined a new class she would be subjected to terrible teasing. The big, bossy bullies would pick on her, point at her, pinch her, and generally make her life miserable.

Sophie never really got used to this bullying. Some-times she was so distressed that she refused to leave her bed. She invented aches and pains, which she learned to describe in realistic detail to the doctors, visiting nurses and social workers called to her bedside. She often wondered at her ability to weave such elaborate stories to adults, when she found it so hard to confront her classmates.

72

But something had to be done. Sophie decided that the best way to demonstrate confidence was to do it on her home turf: she decided to throw a Christmas party. She dreamed up the festive theme herself – it would be a red and green party: red and green balloons, red and green table decorations, and a big cake iced with holly and berries. All the guests would be invited to wear red and green, too.

The next day, Sophie sneaked into the classroom before anyone else had arrived, and deposited invitations, in their red and green envelopes on her classmates' desks.

What a commotion they caused!

The party was the talk of the town. The bossy bullies, of course, were already bragging that they would have the best clothes on the block. People Sophie had never spoken to stopped her in the lunchroom, offering ideas for red and green festive food.

Sophie soon realized that it was easy not to be shy when you are included in the main event, and when you are at the center of it all, your confidence soars.

There was only one tiny detail that Sophie had overlooked. Of course, she had mentioned the party to her parents, but she had not told them what a make-or-break event it was for her. They had never known about Sophie's troubles at school, although they had noticed the new bounce in her step as she set off in the morning. So, when her mother stood at the front door waving goodbye to her, reminding her that they were going to stay with her grandma on the very night of the party, they had no idea what a bomb they had dropped into Sophie's world.

They did not see the color drain from her face, the quiver of her lips, the clenching and unclenching of her fists. They saw nothing of her panic.

"What about my party?" Sophie stammered. "We'll just have to have one for your birthday, dear," her mother replied, turning back into the house and shutting the door.

Cancel the party? She'd rather die! Sophie's mind raced. Her heart thumped. She felt too sick to speak, for a second too shocked even to move.

What could she do? Run! Yes, run – anywhere. Just get away from the situation – as far away as possible.

And that's what she did.

She bought a train ticket into the city. It would be a good place to hide. She had a little pocket money – she'd been saving it up to buy her own red party dress. No one stopped her as she shivered on a seat in the park. No one questioned her as she flicked through the pages of the books in the library. And when the temperature dropped and darkness enveloped the city, she settled down in a doorway and tried desperately to doze off.

At home, her parents were frantic. The police arrived with their tracker dogs and started to scour the area. Helicopters buzzed like giant grasshoppers in the dark skies. The next day at school, everyone in Sophie's class was called in to tell what they knew. The story of the canceled party soon emerged. The bullies in the back row smirked, "So, silly Sophie screws up again!" The rest of the class, shocked and silent, stood in the shadow of their guilt. Poor Sophie, so scared of letting them down. Who cared if the party was on or off? The idea was enough. Sophie was a cool girl and a good friend. They turned on the bully brigade, who for once backed down.

All the way at the back of the classroom, Sophie's mother stood frozen to the spot. Suddenly she saw the true picture. She wept. What could she do to bring Sophie back?

"I'm too frightened to go back," Sophie thought, weak and wobbly, hungry and hurt. She stared sadly at the icy pond and watched the big bossy geese chase the sweet little ducks. She shuddered.

Four frightening days and four frozen nights later.

In just two days it would be Christmas Eve. No tinsel, no turkey, no gift-wrapped treats. Sophie was now too weak to walk. As she gazed up at the soft glow of the streetlight in the darkening sky, she felt her mind drift into a dreamy state. She could hear church bells ringing somewhere, a long way off. *Ding, ding, ding.* She felt weightless, like an angel flying off in a red dress to a brand-new place.

Ding, ding, ding . . .

Bleep, bleep, bleep . . .

Eyes flicker open.

Shapes, soft colors, rosy reds, cool leafy greens, and lots and lots of white.

Eyes gently closing.

A nice new place.

Bleep, bleep, bleep . . .

The hospital machine checking her breathing.

"Sophie," they whispered. She wondered how they knew her name – it must be magic.

"Sophie, Sophie, come home now."

Eyes wide open now. Faces circling her. Her mother and father, silver teardrops on their skin, and through the glass her classmates dressed in red and green – anxious faces, breaking into broad grins. A sea of shapes smiling and waving through the windows of her hospital room. And red and green balloons, everywhere.

As Sophie had drifted off, a passerby had spotted the huddled mass and gently lifted her up, rushing her to the hospital. He had recognized her from the TV appeal that her parents had made, organized by the National Missing Persons Helpline.

A week later, Sophie was the center of attention all over again. Shy little Sophie, surrounded by TV cameras, did not stammer or stumble. She looked straight into the camera and thanked everyone for her special Christmas party in the hospital. And then she spoke slowly and a little sadly. She said, "No matter what is happening in your life, face it, sort it out. Never, ever run away."

Just Another Statistic?

Around Christmastime, if a person has lost contact with someone they care about, they are constantly reminded of it by the advertisements and programs on television showing happy families sharing the Christmas spirit. This can only make the sense of loss bigger.

Christmas is also a time when runaway teenagers, far away from home, may wish that things could have been different. More than 250,000 people are reported missing in the UK each year. Many turn up safe and well within seventy-two hours – but thousands seem to just vanish.

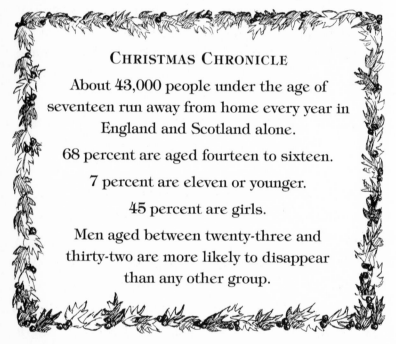

CHRISTMAS CHRONICLE

About 43,000 people under the age of seventeen run away from home every year in England and Scotland alone.

68 percent are aged fourteen to sixteen.

7 percent are eleven or younger.

45 percent are girls.

Men aged between twenty-three and thirty-two are more likely to disappear than any other group.

Around the world missing persons organizations have been set up to try to reunite families. The Salvation Army's Family Tracing Service concentrates on bring relatives together, especially around Christmastime.

The National Missing Persons Helpline (NMPH) was

set up in the UK in 1992, by two sisters: Janet Newman and Mary Asprey. Its main job is to help and support the families of people who have vanished. The NMPH is there to take a message from the runaway and pass it on to relatives to let them know that they are alive and well. It also works with the police, social workers, and hospitals, and has links with international organizations. Around 100,000 people call the charity every year. The NMPH has over 20,000 cases that have not yet been solved, but 70 percent of all cases are solved in the end.

Why Run?

- People may have problems at home, school, or work.
- They may owe money or have had an argument with someone.
- They may be worried about something in particular – something that they cannot face, such as exams at school.
- A few people may suffer from a disease called amnesia: they completely lose their memory.
- Some people just decide that they want to start a new life.

ANGELA HOLLAND WORKS FOR THE NATIONAL MISSING PERSONS HELPLINE. SHE SAYS:

"Christmas is our busiest time of year, because we are given so much coverage on the television and in national

newspapers. It is the time of year when everyone wants to bring people together and reunite families, because these make good Christmas stories. After hearing about the charity, people come to us to ask for help. Just after Christmas a twelve-year-old girl from Yorkshire called Lindsay ran away from home. She had been bullied at school and one day turned to her friend and said that she'd had enough. The friend thought she meant that she was going home. In fact, she was planning to run away. She had stopped going to school, telling her teachers that she was ill. The school didn't think much of it. But, because she'd been ill a community nurse made a regular check on her family home. Thinking she'd been found out, she ran away. Her parents were frantic, police scoured the area. She was found safe and well but was too frightened to go back – she thought her parents would hate her. Of course, her parents were just glad to have her back. Afterwards she went on TV saying that she had not realized how much pain she had caused, and that running away from her problems had only made them worse.

"Often we have to speak for the families, because they are not used to being in the limelight – suddenly they are being asked questions in front of lights and cameras."

"The NMPH respects the fact that the people it helps often want to remain anonymous. When a sixteen-year-old girl found out that she had been featured on a TV program she was furious with her parents. She contacted them and threatened that if they tried to find her again, *she would cut off contact with them completely.*

Some stories do not end happily. It's so sad when children call up hoping you can find a father that they've never seen. Sometimes they don't have a name or a birth certificate. Hearing the disappointment in their voices when they find out there is very little that we can do is heartbreaking."

A Christmas Call Home

A twenty-one-year-old called Phil saw himself on a TV program and called the NMPH helpline. On Christmas Day he was persuaded to call his mother and father to tell them that he was fine. Phil had run away because he had a successful older brother and he could not take the pressure he felt was put on him to succeed.

A Brand-New Identity

A fifteen-year-old boy vanished from his home and was found selling a magazine set up to help the homeless. He had moved to a different city, pretending he was eighteen. He had also changed his name and told everyone that his parents had thrown him out. Only when a local TV program featured his picture was he discovered. The boy had been worried about school and had run away. He returned home to work out his problems.

Message Home

Sometimes, just when runaways get as far away as they want to, they change their minds. Often they are too frightened to pick up the telephone and phone home.

Message Home is a free helpline service in the UK for people who have left home, but want to send a message to their families.

Who Uses Message Home?

● Children and teenagers running away from care (children's homes):

They might say:

"Sorry we have run away . . . as soon as we get some money we want to come back, but we are scared."

● People running away from problems at home:

They might say:

"I'm still alive, but I want no contact with my parents – I'm better off without them."

● Children and teenagers who want to go back, but are unsure how their parents will react if they do go home:

They might say:

"Please ask them if I can come back home – I miss them."

Homecoming: Christmas Eve

Christmas Eve – a time of joy and excitement around the world – unless, that is, you're far away from home, lost and alone, living with a bad decision you made many months before. That Christmas Eve was cheerless and pretty grim for one teenager, Amy, standing shivering alone on a bitterly cold city street. Why wasn't she at home with the rest of her family, huddled around a Christmas tree, peaking at parcels plastered with gaudy gift tags made out to her? Because she had walked out of her home around six months earlier to be with her boyfriend, after her parents had forbidden her to date him.

Amy had only known the man for a couple of months, but there had been something about him that had made her feel glamorous and grown-up. He treated her exactly how she felt – like an adult. OK, so he was over ten years older than she was. So what? Who would want to date any of the boys her own age? Her mother and father had been worried that he might persuade her to leave school. Well, he had assured her that she would learn a lot more about life in the big wide world than she would ever learn at school. And, foolishly, she had believed him. The boyfriend had convinced her to sneak out of her home one night and run away with him.

The sixteen-year-old had been promised a glittering life in a grown-up world. But that was not how it had worked out. Instead she had spent day after day, either looking after her boyfriend – a man she no longer liked or even recognized – or plodding around the streets of the dismal and dirty city, desperately looking for work.

She was so lonely. She spent most of her waking hours alone. Every day she thought of her family – she wondered if they were angry with her. Perhaps they missed her a little bit, too.

As Christmas drew closer, she became more withdrawn and depressed. This made her boyfriend want to stay away from her even more. The terrified teenager had not seen him or anyone else for four days, when she decided to shelter from the icy rain in a wrecked telephone booth. The wind howled through the smashed glass door. She tried not to lean against the filthy walls. Her eyes closed and then opened in a start – she was falling asleep standing on her feet!

As her eyes began to focus, she saw the word "home" clearly standing out on the telephone wall. She pulled the card out from behind all the others pinned to the telephone booth wall. The card advertized a helpline for people just like her – people who wanted to contact their families, but were too afraid to pick up the phone.

Shaking and barely able to make her wobbly words heard above the sound of the traffic rushing to be home before midnight, she dialed the number on the card. Surely no one would be there just hours before Christmas Day?

The line rang, once, twice, then a voice greeted her in a tone that she had not heard for months – it was soft, soothing and very, very kind. The teenager told her story, sobbing, struggling to get the words out. The voice did not judge her, it just asked firmly if she wanted

to go home. Of course she did! The voice promised to telephone her family and explain the situation to them.

She stood in the phone booth and waited. What if they didn't want her back? Where would she go? What would she do? The big clock on the station wall opposite her booth tick-tocked its way toward the best day of the year. Her heartbeat ticked loudly with it.

Dring! The telephone bell crashed through her thoughts. She seized the receiver, pressing it to her ear. It was her father – his voice sounded strangely distant and a little odd. She realized that he must have been crying. Wait in the coffee bar in the station, she was told – the whole family was being packed into the car then and there. They were all driving down to meet her – after all, he said, *she* was the best Christmas present any family could ever want!

The teenager sped across the road to the safety of the coffee bar – terrified, thrilled. Suddenly, she knew Christmas was only a moment away!

CHAPTER FIVE

Homeless

Why Are People Homeless?

Thousands of years ago our ancestors began to build houses in groups – they realized that living together gives people a sense of belonging. People feel more secure: they can help each other out and enjoy each other's company.

Today, more than 100 million people in the world have no home. People become homeless for many reasons:

- If they have no job, they cannot afford to pay for a home.

- Around 14 million people are on the move. They are called migrants or refugees. These people may be running away from a war or a natural disaster such as an earthquake.

87

- Some people leave home because they are frightened to stay where they are. They may have been bullied or attacked.

No Place Like Home

Wars rip families apart. One moment a family has a routine and life seems fairly normal. The next moment, that same family is gathering what possessions they can carry and running for their lives. Some children become separated from their parents in the middle of this chaos. Charities such as *Save the Children* work hard to trace the scattered members of the families and get them back together.

1 Children tell the charity details about themselves, such as their name, age, and where they used to live.

2 Photographs are taken and the information is fed into a computer, where it is stored.

3 Lists of children and photographs are taken to public meetings. The charity uses posters, TV, and radio coverage in its attempt to contact the parents of lost children.

4 If the parents are found they have to be checked out to make sure that they really are the child's parents.

This process goes on even at Christmas. War rarely stops because it is Christmas Day.

Charities all around the world work hard to make Christmas special for everyone.

CHRISTMAS CHRONICLE

70 percent of all homeless children in the US never finish high school.

Pack Up Your Possessions

Imagine that you have to pack up all your possessions into one bag: what would you take? What would you leave behind and why?

Think about:

Keeping yourself warm:
Take clothes that are not too bulky, but that will keep you warm.

Keeping yourself comfortable:
Take shoes that keep your feet warm, but do not make them overheat – shoes that dry out easily if they get wet.

Occupying your time:
Take a book, a Walkman, and a portable game.

89

Remembering your home:
Take pictures of your home, your neighborhood, and your friends.

Make a list of the things left behind that you think you would really miss.

Life Is Not Sweet When You Sleep on the Street
In the UK around two thousand people sleep on the streets every night. Thousands more people throughout the world spend their nights looking for comfort in the streets of big cities.

The charity *Crisis* began its work in 1972. The Crisis London Open Christmas (LOC) has a special program of events between December 23 and 30. Homeless people in London are invited to spend a little time with others. They are given the security, warmth, and food that other people take for granted at Christmastime. The charity gives people a touch of human kindness along with sensible advice and help.

Open Christmas happens all over Britain. There are twenty-nine shelters from Aberdeen in Scotland to Truro in Cornwall, giving help to around three thousand homeless people.

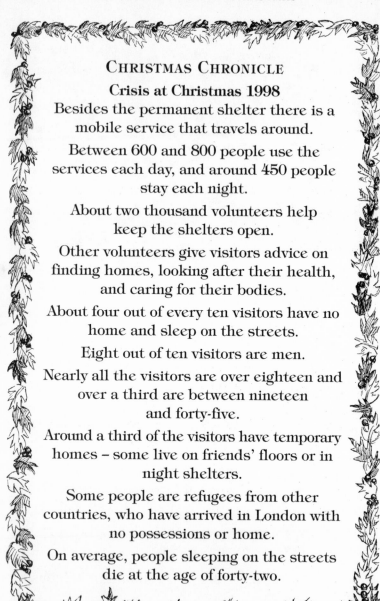

CHRISTMAS CHRONICLE

Crisis at Christmas 1998

Besides the permanent shelter there is a mobile service that travels around.

Between 600 and 800 people use the services each day, and around 450 people stay each night.

About two thousand volunteers help keep the shelters open.

Other volunteers give visitors advice on finding homes, looking after their health, and caring for their bodies.

About four out of every ten visitors have no home and sleep on the streets.

Eight out of ten visitors are men.

Nearly all the visitors are over eighteen and over a third are between nineteen and forty-five.

Around a third of the visitors have temporary homes – some live on friends' floors or in night shelters.

Some people are refugees from other countries, who have arrived in London with no possessions or home.

On average, people sleeping on the streets die at the age of forty-two.

Sorry, Come Back Tomorrow . . .

One visitor to the Christmas shelter in London was very sick. He had not been accepted by any hostels, so he had ended up sleeping on the Strand – a posh London Street – for nine months. He said:

"The only thing left for me now is a couple of cold weather shelters . . . You explain your situation, they phone round the hostels, 'Sorry, nothing, come back tomorrow.' So you come back at the end of the week, still nothing."

The help given at Christmas by Crisis includes lending an ear to people who may have given up hope. Many have lost interest in themselves. One visitor said:

"I don't eat properly. Some days I don't eat at all. Sometimes a few biscuits . . . Sometimes I ask people for change to eat . . . You start losing interest in yourself – not caring about anything, trying to live day by day."

Crisis does not just provide doctors and health workers to care for people who have been neglected. There are other services, too. People can have a haircut, a massage, or just spend time doing something other than trying to survive, such as writing or painting. At Christmas in 1998 Crisis also helped a hundred people find new homes right away.

For these people, finding a home is the best Christmas present of all.

"Being at Crisis Open Christmas has restored my faith in human nature. I've been treated with respect – something I'm not used to. They bent over backwards to help me find accommodation. I'm determined to get myself back together and help others too."

RICHARD, AGE 36

"I'm here because I'm homeless. I've nowhere to go. My house burned down and I lost everything. Without a home it's so difficult – you're going from day to day, wondering what you're going to do next . . . They've given me a roof over my head, comfort, someone to talk to – they're very good like that. The people here appreciate how difficult it is being homeless, and they're comfortable about that. They provide everything here . . . it's the first time I've felt comfortable for nearly a year."

ALLISON, AGE 32

"You come here and you get rid of all your problems. It gives you the security you don't get on the streets, and you can meet friends, talk to people, and sort out any medical problems. I've even had my toenails cut for the first time! What these people do means more than anything. We're strangers, pure strangers, and they've given up their Christmas for us."

KIERAN, AGE 56

"Sleeping on a mattress is better than sleeping on the floor or in cardboard on the pavement. There is no wind blowing in your face . . ."

SUE, AGE 18

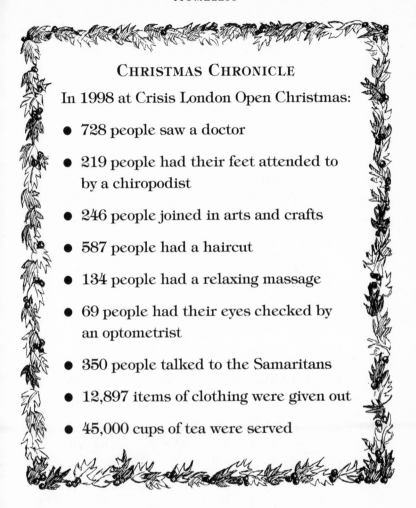

CHRISTMAS CHRONICLE

In 1998 at Crisis London Open Christmas:

- **728** people saw a doctor

- **219** people had their feet attended to by a chiropodist

- **246** people joined in arts and crafts

- **587** people had a haircut

- **134** people had a relaxing massage

- **69** people had their eyes checked by an optometrist

- **350** people talked to the Samaritans

- **12,897** items of clothing were given out

- **45,000** cups of tea were served

Home in time for Christmas:

Crisis has set up *SmartMove*, which helps people find a home and keep it:

"I left home at fifteen, and I've been homeless on and off for eight years now. I didn't want to be given a house –

what I wanted was help in finding one for myself. So I went to SmartMove. The thing is, they ask you what you want, and if they can help they will. I've slept on the streets, and I'd rather be homeless than lose my two dogs, Sam and Zak. SmartMove helped me find a place where all three of us could live. When you're homeless you're surrounded by people everywhere you go. What I like best about having my own home is privacy: closing the front door, putting the hot water on, running the bath, and reading a favorite magazine with a bar of chocolate. That's the best thing in the world!"

All over the world charities set up shelters at Christmas.

The *American Red Cross* helps bring aid to areas that have been struck by disaster, such as wars and earthquakes. *HomeAid America* (website; http://www.home-aid.org/) is an organization that builds shelters for homeless people across America. It realizes that if there are no homes available, you have to go out and build them – and that is exactly what it does!

The Center for the Homeless – Where Miracles Become Reality
(website: http://www.center-for-homeless.com/)

This center has been set up to help the homeless in America. At Christmas the place is full of people who have nowhere else to go. Many have problems with alcohol and drugs.

- At Christmas the center is home to over forty children. The aim is to give children a stable and safe place to spend Christmas and a taste of hope for the future. The center also runs schools so that children can learn what they need to know to make their own lives better.

- One twenty-nine-year-old mother saw her twelve-year-old daughter give birth to a child in the center!

- A boy from a very poor background worked his way to stardom. He was picked to play basketball in the NBA and played professionally for six years, but everything fell apart in his life when his career ended. He became homeless and addicted to drugs. He had lost everything. At the center he found the hope and help he needed to start again.

- An eighty-seven-year-old man who used to be a priest found himself lost and alone. The center took him in and gave him the kindness he needed.

CHAPTER SIX

Reaching Out

Deciding to do something different at Christmas is a big step. It takes courage and a warm, generous spirit to decide to volunteer to help people and animals in need. There are all sorts of imaginative ways to help.

Diary of a Crisis Volunteer, Jane Stevens

Somewhere in the back of my mind, helping Crisis at Christmas had been lurking for as long as I can remember. When my daughter announced she wanted to stay put in her own home on Christmas Day, I asked my sons if they'd like to go there for their Christmas dinner. They both said yes, so I was finally off the hook, and rang Crisis for a volunteer pack.

December 20

I went into the kitchen, not realizing how familiar I was to become with it . . . I made a vegetable curry and portioned the leftovers from a sheik's banquet – it being Ramadan and there being lots of wonderful leftovers, delivered by limousine . . .

December 24 – Christmas Eve

First duty was arranging chocolates on trays for a teatime treat. Then stirring forty gallons of custard – the quantities are amazing. Some guests asked for fruit instead of pudding, so Malc [another volunteer] suggested that the two of us get big baskets and fill them with fruit. We took them out – the baskets emptied in seconds, right before our eyes. Guests kept stuffing their pockets full like they would with sweets. When I got home I thought about how people who feed themselves from trash cans would be sick when they were first fed at the shelter. Their stomachs would not be used to the meal portions. Then I thought how at the end of the week these same people would be hungry when they went back to scavenging, begging, or whatever . . .

December 25 – Christmas Day

I had to use the rear entrance – the police were at the front. I'd missed the fight the previous night. A guest had spent the night in the police cells and was trying to get back in . . . I carved fifteen turkeys myself, and there were at least eight of us carving . . . Harrods helped by sending in loads of goodies, salads and fresh salmon. People were thanking me personally for the lovely food. I kept telling them it was Harrods, but no one was listening.

December 28

I was following Chef's instructions and in charge of thirty-five trays of roast potatoes when a volunteer pointed at me and announced that I hadn't done any washing up! I had a private giggle at the silliness, but considering the number of different personalities, opinions, and backgrounds, there was very little pettiness. I heard today that the £1,000 [$1,600] worth of bacon and sausages that should have been here for Christmas breakfast had left Marks and Spencers but had gone missing en route – quite unbelievable.

December 29

We were short of volunteers today – only seven in the kitchen as opposed to the usual fifteenish. This was OK while cooking – but the clearing up!

We'd completely run out of biscuits and bread (just enough for breakfast and packed lunch sandwiches), and then the coffee ran out in the refreshment area. I found lots of jars in the volunteers' kitchen and so I redirected them. I also found thousands of chocolate "mis-shapes" in the garage, so we laid out trays of them for tea and told the night shift that there were enough for each guest to have a pack in their take-away bag tomorrow. What was interesting was that when the chocolates had first been put out earlier in the week they had all gone. Today, however, the white chocolate nut-covered logs came back untouched. Within a few days the guests had become discriminating.

Chicken pans were going to be terrible to clean, so I laid out about ten and filled them with cold water to soak. Malc asked, would I boil some eggs for tomorrow's egg mayonnaise sandwiches and then produce 450 of them? Egg peeling eventually got everyone giggling and making silly jokes – there were five peeling them, and me mashing. By 10:45 p.m. we gave in and handed the task over to the night shift.

January 1

I think to myself: why can't the country be run like Crisis? Why can't people of all ages, cultures, nationalities, and colors work together every day for the greater good?

I also think how sad it is that volunteers to Crisis have to provide references and police checks. Yes, I understand why they are necessary, but it is still a sorry reflection on our society.

It's New Year's Day and they telephone me from the extension shelter to ask me if I could do any shifts. They have no volunteers for January 6,7,8,10,11, and 12. I tell them that I must make business appointments to keep a roof over our heads and that I will go in when I can. I do want to help every day, but . . .

Give a Little Bit – It's Better Than Taking

Not everyone needs a present they can hold in their hands at Christmas.

COLLEEN TABER FROM MIAMI, FLORIDA, HAS THIS TO SAY:

"One of the most wonderful gifts I received this Christmas was the gift of "no gift," or actually the gift of generosity. A donation was given in my name to the Make-A-Wish Foundation. I was very moved by that gesture and have decided to do something similar next year. Instead of focusing on what to give everyone, make a gift of love: donate in their names to a favorite charity."

Giving something back at Christmas is what another American charity – *Toys for Tots* – is all about. Marines collect and hand out toys to poor children. Their goal is to "Bring the joy of Christmas to America's needy children." Every year Marines hand out millions of toys at Christmas, making Christmas brighter for millions of children.

CHRISTMAS CHRONICLE

The story behind Toys for Tots

1947: Diane Hendricks made a doll that she wanted to give to a child as a Christmas present, but there was no organization to hand the doll over to. So her husband, Major Bill Hendricks decided to set one up himself. He created Toys for Tots, which collected five thousand toys and then handed them out to children in need.

1948: Walt Disney designed the Toys for Tots train logo and the first poster. The posters have featured Mickey Mouse, Donald Duck, Dennis the Menace, Bugs Bunny, and the Road Runner.

1949: Movie stars showed their support for the campaign, and this has continued to this day. Famous supporters have included Frank Sinatra and Clint Eastwood.

1959: Toys for Tots went international for the first time. When a typhoon destroyed homes in Nagoya, Japan, the charity came to the rescue.

1970: By this time over 8 million toys were being collected every year.

1990: Toys for Tots was featured on TV – $3 million (£1,875,000) was raised. The US Marine Corps reserve units collected and gave out 7.9 million toys.

1997: The Marines celebrated the Fiftieth Anniversary of Toys for Tots, and over 10 million toys were handed out. Can you imagine how big that pile of toys must have been?

Over the past fifty years, US Marines have distributed 231 million toys to more than 116 million children in need!

103

Making Dreams Come True

Christmas is a time when we all hope our dreams will come true. What do we *really* want – a new outfit, a computer game, the latest toy or gadget?

The *Make-A-Wish Foundation* (web site http://www.wish.org/) was set up to help children and teenagers cope with life-threatening diseases, by granting them as many wishes as possible. This American charity is run by thirteen thousand volunteers in eighty-two groups. Since the foundation was created in 1980 more than fifty thousand wishes have been granted throughout the US. A video clip of the fifty thousandth wish being granted was featured on their website!

It all began in 1980, when a seven-year-old boy from Phoenix, Arizona, suffering from leukemia, desperately wanted to be a police officer. Officers from the Arizona Department of Public Safety granted that wish – they made him his own uniform, complete with a helmet and badge. They even arranged a ride in a helicopter for him. This story inspired volunteers to set up the first Make-A-Wish Foundation.

Today, many of the most popular dreams are for children to meet their favorite celebrities or to go to Space Camp. Some dreams are not difficult to grant, but they mean so much to the child with the dream. Ed from Oklahoma is a fishing enthusiast. His dream came true when he got to go fishing with the host of his favorite fishing program, and the event was televized! One teenage girl's dream came true when she was picked up in a limousine, dressed up as a model for a photo shoot, and then filmed for a television show.

Real Christmas Spirit

On Christmas Day in 1998 the owner of the Druid Inn in Birchover, Derbyshire, UK, served dinner to thirty-five stray animals, specially invited from a nearby dog sanctuary. Brian Bunce, the innkeeper, said: "I asked my head chef to create a 'dog's dinner'."

After a tasting session where six dogs were invited to help decide what was to be served, the chef got to work making a feast for the guests. How was the tasting carried out? Bunce set a table on his terrace, put up Christmas decorations, and then asked his chef – dressed formally in tails for the occasion – to serve the six dogs beef, lamb, turkey, and fish. The most popular dish – beef – was selected for the Christmas Day feast!

An Unusual Christmas Treat

Just before Christmas 1998, Amber the tiger cub paid a visit to the children's unit of the Royal Orthopaedic Hospital in North London. This special Christmas trip was arranged by Sandra Stone, who set up CHATA – the Children in Hospital and Animal Therapy Association. What is it all about? Well, Sandra believes that bringing animals to children in hospitals can make a difference

to how the patients feel. The event can actually help them get better more quickly!

"The animals help a lot. You can feel quite miserable and depressed, being stuck in here, indoors all the time. The animals distract you and relax you. They are something normal to talk about. They really cheered me up."

LOUISA, AGE 11

"Something out of the ordinary like this brings everyone together. It's a new focus – in a place of illness, operations, and pain."

CHRIS HENRY, UNIT MANAGER

People who give a little bit at Christmas will find that they get a lot back themselves!

At Christmastime and throughout the whole year, remember this too: some people around the world have lost the things they *really* need to help them have a happy life. You can make a difference to them. Give a little bit – it really is better than taking.

CHAPTER SEVEN

Safe and Sound

What is more heartwarming than a sad story with a happy ending?

Of course, some things that seem lost miraculously get found at this time of year. This may be because people make more of an effort to find what's missing in their lives. It may also be because there really is a magical spirit that makes people care. Then again, people may just have a little bit more time to reflect, remember, and think about what really is important in their lives and in the world.

Here are twelve stories – one for each of the twelve days of Christmas. Each one will remind you that although Christmas for some is a time of great joy and for others a time of great hardship, when we keep hope in our hearts and show goodwill toward others, some stories can have happy endings.

12

The tree was aglow with tinsel and lights – all set for the big day. Who would have thought disaster was just around the corner? Not Shannon Perry from Boston, Massachusetts, as she drove her children to school just before Christmas. When she arrived home she discovered to her horror that the tree had been wrecked and the lights were gone! Who would have done such a thing, and why? Shocked, she realized the truth: Monty the six-month-old golden retriever puppy had eaten everything – including the wire and bulbs! She rushed the dog to the vet, convinced they would have to operate to get the lights out. But surgeon Richard Goldman had other ideas. He decided to wait and see if the little lights reappeared out the other end of the mischievous little puppy. They X-rayed Monty to check on

the lights' progress – finally, out they popped. The lost lights had been found – danger over!

11

It had been nothing special for Jean Crawley – just an early-morning winter walk along the cliff at Ravenscar in North Yorkshire, UK, to clear her head. Jean had left the guesthouse she was staying in with her husband, Reg, and set off at a leisurely pace along the cliffs, with Brandy, her dog.

On their way back, Jean had bent down to tie her shoelace. When she looked up, Brandy was gone. He must have run off into that small cluster of trees on the cliff top, she thought. She waited, then walked toward the trees, calling his name. Silence – no familiar Brandy bark. Perhaps he had gone over the edge!

Brandy could never have survived that fall – could he?

Jean's heart raced, She felt white with fear – she was convinced her beloved Brandy was dead! She ran for help and combed the area with Reg, even lying flat on her stomach and peering over the sheer drop. There was no sign of him. She wept – Brandy, the tan-and-black mongrel, the stray who had followed a neighbor all the way home and refused to go away, had finally gone. After three and a half years it was a hard blow.

The couple had no choice – they went home and tried to come to terms with the sudden loss. How do you cope with a shock like that? One way was to get rid of all the painful reminders that Brandy was gone. So his favorite playthings – his little teddy bear, and the toy penguin – were passed on to their son's dogs. But they kept a memento: the photo of Brandy stayed in its special place in the living room.

Meanwhile, Brandy was getting used to his new life, too.

Yes, he *had* fallen over the cliff, but he had landed on a narrow ledge halfway down. Stunned, bruised, but determined to survive, the dog had crawled up and down, making a deep path, desperately looking for a way out. And there he stayed, lapping up pools of rainwater and munching grass, leaves, and bracken. And he waited.

And he waited. *For a month, he waited!*

Finally, he was spotted by a fisherman, who called the coast guard and the RSPCA. A dramatic rescue

111

operation began. The coast guard used thick ropes and climbing equipment to abseil down the cliff and pluck brave Brandy to safety.

Apart from being a little bruised, tired, and very, very hungry, Brandy was fine. He was taken to an animal rescue center, and when he was finally reunited with Jean and Reg there were more tears all around and a gigantic wag of the tail from Brandy. It was a miracle! The neighbors were thrilled, and the TV cameras paid a visit.

Brandy was found, and so happy to be home. Jean and Reg were spared the agony of spending Christmas without the family's best friend.

10

When you want to change your situation, it's good to look for help and advice – but sometimes making up your own mind and taking the plunge is the best thing to do. Take a tip from a duck that found herself in danger just days before Christmas in 1998.

Molly was stuck to the ice of her favorite pond. She had been there for ages, unable to move. Finally some local people noticed and jumped into action, calling out three fire engines and frogmen in special diving suits. It seemed that everyone wanted to save Molly the duck – after all, it was the season of goodwill to all creatures, even feathered ones.

An inflatable bridge was made and pushed out onto the ice. The two divers carefully crawled across the bridge, trying to get to the duck – but just before they reached her, Molly flapped her wings and flew into the sky, leaving the rescue team looking pretty silly! Making a great effort, she had forced herself off the ice – Molly had decided to save herself!

9

Andrew Wilcox, a friend, and Patch – his five-year-old border collie – had set out on a boat trip that they would never forget. As they chugged along the River Trent near Stoke Bardolph in Nottinghamshire, UK, their trip was turned into turmoil. The engine suddenly died, and the boat and its party of people plunged over a raging weir. The two men were rescued and taken to the hospital – they were freezing cold from their ordeal in the icy water. But they thought Patch must have been swept away by the strong river current. Andrew knew his dog was special. As he lay in his hospital bed, his mind raced: maybe Patch had managed to swim to the bank and was out there, somewhere, trying to find his way home? Or maybe he had struggled against the force of the water, lost his strength, and been swept away. Maybe he was floating out to sea – dead.

Thirty-six hours after the boat had capsized in the rushing water, police divers moved in to drag the upturned boat to the surface and back to the bank. To their amazement, as they flipped the boat over, Patch swam to the surface. He had found a pocket of air in the hull of the boat, and even though he was underwater, he had used this air to stay alive. Patch and Andrew were reunited for Christmas!

8

Three years ago poor Buster was locked up behind bars. What had he been charged with? His crime, under Section One of the UK's Dangerous Dogs Act, was that he was a Staffordshire Bull Terrier. Yet he had never bitten a soul! Buster's owner, Sandra Rowlands, had been fighting his case, but it had taken three years for her lawyer to convince the authorities that poor Buster was not dangerous at all.

After all that time in police kennels, Buster was thin and in poor health. Bruised, scarred, and with his tail split, the sad dog was welcomed home and helped to recover. Buster made friends with Buster 2 – another Stafford – and Sandra and her five-year-old daughter were on top of the world: "I can't believe how quickly he adapted to being back with us." said Sandra. "Buster's the top dog. It will be the best Christmas ever!"

7

In December 1944 a taste of Christmas was delivered to children whose whole lives had been darkened by a war that had been going on for nearly five years. Some French, Belgian, and Dutch children had never known Christmas. Others had forgotten the thrill they used to feel on Christmas morning. The Royal Canadian Air Force, stationed a long way from home in Europe, invited two hundred children to

their air base. They arranged a film show, a visit from Santa Claus himself, a decorated Christmas tree, wrapped presents, and a feast of sandwiches, cakes, sausages, and – the biggest treat of all – ice cream! The soldiers had received many packages from their families back home, and they had decided to share their treats with the children.

The party caused a storm. Hundreds of hungry, sad little children had heard the news and gathered outside, hoping for a party of their own. And that's exactly what they got!

6

The robin did not always have such a startling red breast. The story goes something like this:

When Joseph set out from the stable to find firewood to keep Mary and their new son warm, the fire's flames very nearly died away. They were saved by a group of tiny birds that gathered around the fire, fanning it to keep the embers alight. The fire came back to life, burning the poor birds' feathers. Mary was so grateful, she magically turned their feathers bright red!

5

Geoff Smith, aged thiry-seven, spent 142 days in a tiny box under the garden of the Railway Inn in Mansfield, Nottinghamshire, UK. A giant tube connected him to the outside world. Through it he could receive food and drink and talk to people. He was there to break the world record for staying underground, set by an American in 1981. He also managed to beat his own mother's record set in 1968 – she stayed underground for one hundred days. He donated all the money he received in sponsorship to the RSPCA.

Spending Christmas underground meant that Geoff missed out on all the celebrations, but when he emerged at the end of January 1999 he could celebrate his new world record. On reaching the surface, he said: "I'll not be buried again until I'm carried away in my real coffin." Who can blame him! The event had given him so much time to think about his life. It had made him a celebrity for a while – television crews and newspaper reporters had gathered at the place. The event had changed his life forever.

4

Helena was a soft-spoken woman, but she loved to tell her story of the greatest gift she ever received. Helena had lived with her family in a tiny two-room thatched hut in Cochabamba, Bolivia, for eight years. Her old home was flimsy, dark, and also dangerous. Helena found out just in time that one of the few decorations on the wall – a faded calendar – actually covered up a hole that housed a deadly pest known as the "kissing bug." This nasty bug had actually wiped out over twenty thousand people in Central and South America. The horrible creepy creature made its home in the cracks of mud walls or in thatched roofs. It popped out, biting its victims just like a mosquito. Helena found out just in time – she was one of the lucky ones.

Helena was desperate for a new start. But how could she afford to build a new home? The miracle happened when a group called *Habitat for Humanity* contacted her and offered to build her a brand-new home.

This group works throughout the world to build people in need simple, safe homes that they can afford. Volunteers give up their time to help build homes for people who really need them. People, groups, and businesses also donate money for materials and land.

A few days before Christmas, Helena stood in the doorway of her new home telling her story. She was happy to pay back the small loan she had on her Habitat home by working in the fields. She was proud that she could contribute in this way. And as Christmas approached she thanked God for her good fortune – after all, her very special gift had more than likely saved her life.

3

Christmas Eve, and a small boy arrived outside a tiny house in the heart of a comfortable neighborhood. The curtains were drawn tightly, and the muffled sounds of a television show seeped through the cracks beneath the door. Inside, the family was gathered – relaxed, happy.

The tiny child was holding a piece of string. The piece of string was tied loosely around the collar of his black-and-white puppy. Both puppy and boy shivered on the steps. Standing on tiptoes, the boy reached up to press the doorbell. The bell played a jingle-jangle version of *We Wish You a Merry Christmas*. The tune cut through the frozen silence.

The boy shuddered, suddenly unsure. He looked down as the door opened and a wonderful warmth wrapped itself around him and his little dog.

A moment later, inside by the fire, he told his tale. His parents had argued. His mother was crying, his father was hurling furniture and shouting, and he was very,

very scared. So, terrified, he had slipped out of his home, and come to the only place he knew he would be welcome. After all, the family had helped him in the past when his dog was sick – he knew they would not turn him away.

The boy was right. The lady telephoned his mother, who arrived quickly, and then mother, son, and dog stayed bundled up, safe and warm, waiting for Christmas morning.

Christmas Eve, and a young man arrived at a tiny house and pressed the bell. The jingle-jangle tune made him smile. The door opened, and he was greeted with a hug. After all, the man was no stranger – he made the same special trip every year – visiting the family that had not turned him away one snowy Christmas Eve a long time ago.

2

The group of children sat quietly in the wooden hut. The rain pounding on the tin roof mingled with the tinkling bells of the sleigh outside.

No one whispered a word. The sound of the bells grew louder and louder – until suddenly the door creaked open. There stood a very old man, dressed from head to foot in scarlet red. His hat was pulled down over ears, and his long, white beard, covered in raindrops, curled curiously into an "S" shape. He looked around the silent room, his gaze lingering on each child's tiny expectant face.

"Merry Christmas," he said. Silence. He took his hat off and faced them, mouthing the words and moving his hands quickly at the same time. The children cheered and clapped. You see, they had not heard the rain on the roof, the sleigh bells, or the whispered message. But they had understood him at last when they read his lips and watched his fingers spelling out his greeting.

Santa was there, and he wished them well.

The ten children shared two very important things: first they were all beside themselves with excitement because it was Christmas Eve; and second, none of them could hear – they were all deaf. Of course, that did not mean they could not communicate – most of them could lip-read and sign very well. They also used their faces to show how they felt. When Santa walked past them with his bells jingling they could feel the vibrations of the sound, they could sense the Christmas magic he brought with him.

After pacing the room, Santa placed himself very close to the semicircle of children, and making sure he could be seen by them all, he start giving out his gifts. All the while he signed to them, indicating when it was time for each child to come forward and collect his or her own special present.

Finally, there was only one present left. A small dark-haired boy hovered at the end of the line of happy faces. Recognizing his name being spelled out in sign language, he came forward and slowly took the present.

121

He signed a "Thank you" to Santa for coming to visit them. Then he spelled out this message: "Do you know what I really want for Christmas this year? I want everyone in the world to be able to talk to us just like Santa has. I want everyone we meet to be able to speak with their hands and their faces, so that they can share in our world and we can share in theirs."

Santa and the semicircle of smiling children stood up and applauded. Yes, that would really be the best Christmas present of all!

1

Almost a hundred years ago a small boy, not yet five years old, spent his life wandering the streets of London. He knew most of the city's boarding houses. If you asked him he would tell you which had the best kitchen with the biggest fire. His first language was street slang, picked up as he roamed the streets with his mother, a destitute tramp with no home, friends, or family. Billy's life was spent begging for a penny or halfpenny or stealing "pudden" from bread shops to keep himself alive.

But Billy found it so hard to protect himself on the streets of London. When other boys, two or three years older than himself, pounced on him and seized the food that he had struggled so hard to find, all he could do was sit and scowl, his little fists clenched, ready for a fight.

That was Billy's life, until just before Christmas 1901, when he was plucked from the streets and offered a place in the country in a home belonging to Dr. Barnardo.

At that point, Billy's life changed forever . . .

Billy opened his eyes and blinked. He might be five – well nearly five, anyway – but he knew what was what, and this was not the East End of London. These were not the cobbled streets that stank of rotten vegetables and the stuff that horses left behind! He was not clutching half a loaf of stale bread that he had found in the gutter the night before.

What a strange smell.

What strange light.

What could it be? It was not unpleasant, it was just so different!

Billy blinked again, then sat up in the little bed and looked around.

Bright wintry light flickered though the crack in the material hanging at the window. "It must be there to keep the light out," he thought to himself. "How strange!"

The small boy looked around him – everything shone. It was like that tiny patch of blue that he sometimes saw between the buildings in London when he looked up. *But it was everywhere.*

His body was covered in a crisp white shirt, and he was . . . *clean!* Yes, clean, everywhere. Not just his fingers, but his toes too!

Billy crept to the window and pulled back the material. The world outside was white. Absolutely white. It must be snow! His mother had told him about this before she died, but he had only ever seen a few flakes settling on the filthy streets of the city, never a blanket like this!

A bell rang close by, and he heard the patter of feet on the stone floors. Voices whispered – he strained to hear the words.

"Merry Christmas to you," they said to each other.

"Christmas" – a word he remembered from somewhere. Where was it? Perhaps he had heard it when he stood in the shadows outside a shop window that was piled high with hams, cold meats, and turkeys. People had stood at that window and talked about "Christmas." What could it be?

He sat and waited. Billy was not afraid. For the first time in his life, he did not feel alone. He also knew that the people around him would not try to take things from him. Perhaps they might even give him something. He scowled, remembering his life on the streets of London.

Just then, a tap on the door was followed by a creak. The door swung open.

A face with a dark beard peered around the door. The face smiled. "Come on, Billy, it's Christmas Day and it's time for a special feast. Come and join us."

Billy smiled.

That's what Christmas is, he thought. *It's the day when people smile.*

Useful Addresses

Here is a handy list of contacts, for people who want more information:

American Society for the Prevention of Cruelty to Animals (ASPCA)
424 East 92nd Street, New York, NY 10128-6804, USA
(212) 876 7700

The Cats Protection League
17 King's Road, Horsham, West Sussex, RH13 5PN, UK
01403 221900

The Center for the Homeless
813 South Michigan Street, South Bend, Indiana 46601, USA
219 282 8700
http://www.center-for-homeless.com

Crisis
42 Adler Street, London E1 1EE, UK
0171 655 8300
e-mail: crisis.uk@easynet.co.uk
internet www.crisis.org.uk

The Dogs' Home Battersea
4 Battersea Park Road, London SW8 4AA, UK
0171 622 3626
http://www.dogshome.org

Friends of the Earth International
P.O. Box 19199, 1000 GD Amsterdam, The Netherlands
0031 20 6221369

Habitat for Humanity International
121 Habitat St., Americus, GA 31709-3498
(912) 924 – 6935
http://www.habitat.org

HomeAid America
http://www.homeaid.org

Hugs for Homeless Animals
P.O. Box 5967
Beaverton, Oregon 97006-0967 USA
e-mail lostfound@h4ha.org
http://www.h4ha.org/

Humane Society of the U.S.
2100 L St., N.W., Washington, DC 20037, USA

Make-A-Wish Foundation
100 West Clarendon, Suite 2200, Phoenix, Arizona
85013, USA
(800) 722-WISH (9474)
http://www.wish.org

Message Home
Freephone Helpline: 0800 700 740

National Missing Persons Helpline
Roebuck House, 284-286 Upper Richmond Road West,
London SW14 7JE, UK
0181 392 4545 or Freecall 0500 700 700

PETA EUROPE (People for the Ethical Treatment of Animals)
P.O. Box 3169, London W1 2JF, UK
0181 785 3113

PETA USA (People for the Ethical Treatment of Animals)
P.O. Box 42516, Washington, DC 20015, USA
(301) 770 – PETA

Pets Lifeline
P.O. Box 341, Sonoma, CA 95476, USA
(707) 996-4577
http://www.petslife.org.
(The shelter is found at 19686 Eighth Street East,
Sonoma.)

Royal Society for the Prevention of Cruelty to Animals (RSPCA)
Causeway, Horsham, West Sussex RH12 1HG, UK
01403 264181

Royal Society for the Protection of Birds (RSPB)
The Lodge, Sandy, Bedfordshire SG19 2DL, UK
01767 680551

Salvation Army
http://www.salvation army.org/worldwid.htm

Toys for Tots
http://www.toysfortots.org

World Society for the Protection of Animals (WSPA)
2 Langley Lane, London SW8 1TJ, UK
0171 793 0540
P.O. Box 190, Boston, MA 02130, USA
(617) 522 7000